KEY TO THE NAMES OF
BRITISH BIRDS

KEY TO THE NAMES OF BRITISH BIRDS

BY

R. D. MACLEOD

LONDON
SIR ISAAC PITMAN & SONS, LTD.

First published 1954

SIR ISAAC PITMAN & SONS, LTD.
PITMAN HOUSE, PARKER STREET, KINGSWAY, LONDON, W.C.2
THE PITMAN PRESS, BATH
PITMAN HOUSE, LITTLE COLLINS STREET, MELBOURNE
27 BECKETTS BUILDINGS, PRESIDENT STREET, JOHANNESBURG

ASSOCIATED COMPANIES
PITMAN PUBLISHING CORPORATION
2 WEST 45TH STREET, NEW YORK

SIR ISAAC PITMAN & SONS (CANADA), LTD.
(INCORPORATING THE COMMERCIAL TEXT BOOK COMPANY)
PITMAN HOUSE, 381–383 CHURCH STREET, TORONTO

MADE IN GREAT BRITAIN AT THE PITMAN PRESS, BATH
E4—(C.174)

ACKNOWLEDGMENTS

FOR all information about birds, except their names, I have relied mainly on other books, particularly *The Handbook of British Birds*, edited by H. F. Witherby. The list of British birds and nearly everything about their appearance, voice, behaviour, habitat and distribution have been taken from that invaluable work; and even with regard to names I have obtained much assistance from its reference to the various authorities.

Other books on which I have particularly relied are given below—

1. Aristotle: *History of Animals*, in the original Greek and D. W. Thompson's English translation.
2. British Ornithologists' Union: *A List of British Birds*, 1915.
3. Coward: *The Birds of the British Isles and their Eggs*.
4. Newton: *A Dictionary of Birds*.
5. Pliny: *Natural History*, in the original Latin and Rackham's English translation.
6. Swainson: *Provincial Names and Folk Lore of British Birds*.
7. Swann: *A Dictionary of English and Folk Names of British Birds*.

In addition I have consulted a great number of dictionaries, reference books and accounts of the circumstances in which a name was originally bestowed; but it is impossible to mention all these individually.

I also owe a great debt to Mr. J. D. Macdonald and his staff in the Bird Room of the South Kensington Natural History Museum; and I have received considerable assistance from the East Sussex County Library and the libraries of the British Museum and University College, London.

R. D. M.

CONTENTS

INTRODUCTORY

THE purpose of this book is twofold: to create and stimulate an interest in the scientific names of British birds, and to explain the meaning and origin of both common names and scientific ones.

It may be asked, What is to be gained by learning scientific names? There are two main advantages. In the first place, scientific names are systematic. They tell us, for instance, the genus to which any bird belongs, and in this way assure us that the bird resembles certain other birds—a connexion that is often not made clear by the corresponding common names. Thus there is no suggestion of connexion between the siskin and the British goldfinch from their common names, but their scientific names, *Carduēlis spinus* and *Carduelis carduelis britannica*, reveal at once that the birds belong to the same genus, *Carduelis*. Conversely, although a close connexion is suggested between the house-sparrow and the British hedge-sparrow by their common names, their scientific names, *Passer domesticus domesticus* and *Prūnella modulāris occidentālis*, show that, in fact, the birds belong to different genera.

The second great advantage of scientific names is that they are current universally, and always denote the same birds, whatever the language or the nationality of the person using them. Whenever, therefore, anyone uses or whenever anyone reads or hears a scientific name, there can be no doubt about the identity of the bird that it is intended to denote. *Erithacus rubecula melophilus* may be a fearful mouthful, but it possesses a supreme merit—it avoids the confusion of plain *robin*, which denotes one bird in England and another in America.

Thus an acquaintance with scientific names is indispensable to a serious study of birds. But to be content with bare acquaintance is to miss much. If, instead of merely memorizing scientific names as symbols, we also inquire into their inherent meaning, we shall find our efforts well rewarded. We shall discover that a scientific name is not just a jumble of letters or an arbitrary sound, but an intelligible expression, and we shall reap a double benefit. We shall not only gratify our reason, but also make the name easier to remember.

Nor is that all. When inquiring into the meaning of a name, we shall naturally also inquire into its origin and derivation; and this too will be well worth while. For some names, particularly the generic ones, have associations that enhance our interest both in the names themselves and in the birds that they denote. Does not *Caprimulgus* signify more to us when we realize that its original meaning is "goat-sucker," which is what the nightjar was long reputed to be? And does not *Nūmēnius* make more appeal to us when we associate it with the "new moon," whose shape the curlew's bill resembles? Common names naturally require less explanation than scientific ones, but many even of the common names conceal an interesting origin. How many people know that the petrel is called after St. Peter from its habit of "walking" on the sea? Or that *linnet* has sprung from the same root as *linen*?

PLAN OF THE BOOK

Apart from the Introduction, the book consists of two lists of names. List I contains the scientific names, List II the common ones. Both lists are in alphabetical order.

In these lists are included all the birds classed as British in Witherby's *Handbook*; and the names assigned to the birds, whether scientific or common, have been taken from the same authority.

About the list of common names, however, two points should be borne in mind. Not all these names are "popular," that is to say, names that have grown up naturally and form part of the everyday talk of ordinary people. On the contrary many of them are no more than "book names," that is to say, names that have been invented by ornithologists and whose use is, for the most part, confined to experts. And, on the other hand, many names that are indubitably popular are omitted from the list; for Witherby gives only one common name for each bird, though many birds are known by different names in different places. If it be asked why it is necessary to follow Witherby in this respect instead of giving an exhaustive list, the answer is obvious. To have included all the provincial names would have so swollen the list of common names as to upset the balance of the book and relegate the scientific names to a very secondary place. Furthermore, to have followed one authority for the scientific names and another for the common ones would have resulted inevitably in inconsistencies and confusion.

Lists I and II each contain 520 names, but over 200 of the birds to which these names refer are very rarely found in the British Isles.

In List I all the species and sub-species of a single genus are grouped together. Against each scientific name is given the corresponding common name, the meaning and derivation of the scientific name as far as they are known, and any note that may be necessary. Points particularly dealt with by such a note are the application of the name, its appropriateness, its history and its associations.

In List II similar principles are followed, but with certain reservations.

Strictly speaking, a common name has no generic, specific or sub-specific term, but it often has the appearance of being made up of a generic and a specific term; e.g. in "willow-warbler" it appears as though "willow" is a specific term, and "warbler" a generic one; and, for the purpose of grouping in the list, these apparent generic and specific terms have been treated as though they were real ones. Thus all the names ending in "warbler" are grouped together in List II, just as all the species and sub-species of *Acrocephalus* are grouped together in List I.

Often the "specific" term of the common name, and sometimes the "generic" term, has the same meaning as the corresponding term of the scientific name; and when this is so, the explanation is, as a rule, not repeated in List II, but must be looked for by the reader in List I. Thus the meaning of "bean" in "bean-goose" is to be found under *Anser fabālis fabalis*.

THE FORM OF SCIENTIFIC NAMES

A scientific name consists of two or, more usually, three terms. The first term indicates the name of the genus to which the bird belongs, the second the name of the species and the third the name of the sub-species. By genus is meant a class that includes various kinds of birds, all of which possess certain essential characteristics in common. Each of the kinds thus included in a genus is called a species, which, in its turn, has certain characteristics that mark it off from all other species. Most species have themselves been recently divided into a number of sub-species, which amount to hardly more than variations and whose basis is mainly geographical. Thus *Mōtacilla alba yarrellii*, which is the scientific name for the pied wagtail, indicates that the bird belongs to the genus *Motacilla* (wagtail), the species *alba* (white) and the sub-species *yarrellii* (the British form, called after the ornithologist, William Yarrell).

The generic term is always a noun. The specific and sub-specific terms are usually adjectives, but sometimes nouns, either in apposition or in the genitive. The genitive is particularly used to commemorate some person connected with the discovery of a species or sub-species, and is usually indicated by the two-syllabled termination, -*ii*, which represents the Latin genitive.

In many names the same term occurs twice, and in some names three times. When the specific term is the same as the generic one, this implies that the species in question is the typical species of that genus. Thus *Carduēlis carduelis britannica*, which is the scientific name of the British goldfinch, implies that this is a form of the typical species of the genus *Carduelis*. Similarly when the sub-specific term is the same as the specific one, this implies that the sub-species in question is the typical sub-species of that species.   Thus *Dryobatēs mājor major*, which is the scientific name of the northern great spotted woodpecker, implies that this is the typical sub-species of the species *Dryobates major*.   When all three terms of a scientific name are the same, this implies that the species is the typical species of the genus and that the sub-species is the typical sub-species of the species.   Thus *Līmōsa limosa limosa*, which is the scientific name of the black-tailed godwit, implies that both the species and sub-species are typical.

The terms of a scientific name have nearly always a Latin form.   Some of these terms are genuine Latin words, others are latinized forms of Greek words and others have been coined from Latin or Greek words by ornithologists.   A few terms, however, have been borrowed from other languages, sometimes in their original form and sometimes latinized.

When a Greek word is latinized, *k* becomes *c*, and *u* becomes *y*: e.g. *hupoleukos* ("whitish" or "white underneath") becomes *hypoleucos*; and (in spite of the instance, just quoted, to the contrary) final *-os* usually becomes *-us*: e.g. *ōtos* (long-eared owl) becomes *otus*.

In List I it will be observed that each scientific name is followed by a person's name.   This indicates that the person is the author of the last term of the scientific name, that is to say, of the specific or sub-specific term, as the case may be.   If the author's name is enclosed in brackets, this indicates that the genus has been changed since the specific name was originally given.   Thus in *Streptopelīa turtur turtur* (Linnæus), the scientific name for "turtle-dove," the name of Linnæus is enclosed in brackets, because he named the bird *Columba turtur* and his specific term has been retained, but the species has been transferred to another genus.

In other books the author's name is often given in an abbreviated form, but for the sake of clearness the name is always given in List I of this book in full.   In List II the author's name has been omitted altogether.

PRONUNCIATION OF SCIENTIFIC NAMES

The pronunciation of scientific names is liable to be a stumbling-block to persons without knowledge of Greek or Latin.   To give full guidance in this book is impracticable;   for, apart from other reasons, the correct pronunciation of Greek and Latin is still a matter of dispute.   It has, however, been found possible to help in two ways: by marking the vowels, where necessary, and by enunciating two general rules.

The main mark that has been used is the one to indicate that a vowel is long.   Thus in *Cucūlus* (L., cuckoo) the middle *u* should be pronounced long, but the other two short.   Another mark used is the diæresis to indicate that the second of two adjoining vowels is to be pronounced separately.

Thus *aëtos* (Gr., eagle) should be pronounced as three syllables, not two. The marks, however, are not repeated unnecessarily. Thus, in List I, no word has its pronunciation marked, directly or indirectly, more than once under each heading.

Of the rules, the main one is that *e* is never mute in Greek or Latin. Thus *exīlipes* (L., thin-footed) should be pronounced as four syllables, not three, and *kephale* (Gr., head) should be pronounced *kephaley*. The second rule concerns the combination *eu*; this is usually pronounced as two sounds in Latin, but as a diphthong in Greek. As a rule of thumb for the purpose of this book, *eu* should be pronounced as two sounds at the end of a word, but as a diphthong at the beginning or in the middle of a word. Thus *rosāceus* (L., rose-coloured) should be pronounced as four syllables, not three, but *leukos* (Gr., white) should be pronounced as two syllables, not three.

If the reader accepts this guidance, he should be able to pronounce scientific names as accurately as most ornithologists.

GENDER OF SCIENTIFIC NAMES

A specific or sub-specific term, when an adjective, has to agree in gender with the generic term. Fortunately, bird names in Latin are all either masculine or feminine, so we need not trouble about the neuter gender. Agreement in gender is effected by the use of the appropriate termination in the specific or sub-specific term.

Much the most common masculine termination of Latin adjectives is *-us*, for which the corresponding feminine termination is *-a*. Thus *Larus marīnus* (masculine), great black-backed gull, but *Pelagodroma marina hypoleuca* (feminine), frigate-petrel. The only other terminations that need be mentioned are the masculine *-er* and the corresponding feminine *-(e)ra*. Thus *Pārus āter ater* (masculine), continental coal-tit, but *Fulica atra atra* (feminine), coot. For all other adjectives used in this book, the masculine and feminine terminations are the same.

Sometimes, indeed, it appears that the specific or sub-specific term does not agree with the gender of the generic term. This may be because the specific or sub-specific term is not actually an adjective, but a noun in apposition. Thus, in *Emberīza cirlus cirlus*, cirl bunting, *cirlus* retains its masculine termination because it is used as a noun. Occasionally, however, the disagreement is simply a mistake. Thus, in *Chlidonias hybrida hybrida*, the whiskered tern, the feminine form *hybrida* is an obvious mistake for the masculine form *hybridus*. Evidently the error arose from the fact that the original name was *Sterna hybrida*, where *hybrida* was quite correct as *Sterna* is a feminine word.

BASIC FORMS OF LATIN AND GREEK NOUNS AND VERBS

Latin and Greek nouns and verbs are inflected, that is to say, their termination changes according to the number and case of a noun and the voice, mood, tense, number and person of a verb. It is usual to specify a noun by the nominative singular and a verb by the first person singular of the present indicative active, and for the most part this rule has been observed in this book. Often, however, bird names are derived not from the nominative of a noun, but from its stem, and this is best seen in the genitive case. Where necessary, therefore, the genitive has been given as well as the nominative case: e.g. *falcinellus* (a species of *Līmicola*) is shown as coming from Latin *falx* (gen. *falcis*), sickle. As regards verbs, the present indicative form should, strictly, be translated as "I do so-and-so," but it has been treated here as the general basic form, and in the English translation the present infinitive has been given instead: e.g. *rīdibundus* (a species of *Larus*) is shown as coming from Latin *rideo*, "to laugh," not "I laugh." Usually the "to" has been omitted, when there is no danger of confusing a verb with a noun.

ORIGIN OF SCIENTIFIC NAMES

The credit for founding the present system of bird nomenclature lies with the Swedish naturalist, Carl von Linné (1707–1778), or, to use the Latin name by which he is generally known, Linnæus. It was he who established the custom of making a bird's name consist of two terms, the first designating the genus and the second the species. Since then the custom has grown up of usually adding a third term to indicate the sub-species, but this is merely a development.

• The general acceptance of the Linnæan system brought about two great improvements. First, for international purposes, a single list of names took the place of the various conflicting names that had been adopted by one country or another, so that henceforth the same name denoted the same bird to every ornithologist throughout the world. And secondly, the names that now came into general use were simple and concise, compared with the cumbrous references that they superseded. Thus Ray (1676), in the title of his account of the shoveler, had given the bird's scientific name as *Anas platyrhynchos altera sive clypeāta Germānis dicta* ("another duck with a broad bill or, according to the Germans, with a shield-like gorget"), and then, in order to make his meaning clear, had gone on to mention the names used by Gesner and Aldrovandus and the common German name; whereas for Linnæus a bare two words sufficed—*Anas clypeata*.

It must not, however, be concluded that because Linnæus invented the names, he also created the material out of which he made them. On the contrary, many of his generic names were current over two thousand years ago, and date back to the days of Ancient Greece or Ancient Rome. For it was in Greece that ornithology was studied for the first time in Europe, and it was through imperial Rome that Greek names, usually in a Latin guise, as well as names of Rome's own creation, spread throughout the world. Some of the works of these early ornithologists are still extant, and two of the writers, Aristotle and Pliny, require special mention.

The Greek philosopher, Aristotle, lived in the fourth century (384–322) B.C. For thirteen years he was president of the Lyceum, which we may regard as "The University of Athens." Amongst his many works was one entitled *History of Animals*. This contains many references to birds, and a good many of the names still survive. Any passage from Aristotle cited in List I should be taken as coming from this work, unless the contrary is stated.

Pliny's *Natural History*, Book X of which is devoted to birds, is the main source of our ancient Latin names. This great Roman lived in the first century (23–79) A.D., and was a man of many parts. Though primarily a man of letters, he was also a man of action, and it was the combination of these two roles that brought him to his death. For as admiral he had the opportunity, and as naturalist the desire, to investigate the eruption of Vesuvius, in which he perished. Any passage from Pliny cited in List I should be taken as coming from his *Natural History*, which is, indeed, his sole surviving work.

Writers of what may roughly be called the Middle Ages who contributed particularly to bird names are: Albertus Magnus (otherwise Groot or Albertus of Cologne, about 1206–1280), who wrote a book *On Animals* in Latin in twenty-six volumes, one of which dealt with birds and was based mainly on Aristotle's works; Theodorus Gaza (about 1400–1475), a Greek who spent most of his life in Italy and translated Aristotle's works on natural history into Latin; and Conrad Gesner (1516–1565), a German-Swiss naturalist who wrote a *History of Animals* in Latin, including a book on birds, which earned for him the title of "The German Pliny."

A few Latin words mentioned in this book are too late to be called Classical, and too early to be called Medieval; these are described as Late Latin.

In addition to the names that may fairly be described as genuine Latin, there are names now in use, particularly specific and sub-specific ones, that never formed part of living Latin, but were coined by ornithologists. Unfortunately, ornithologists are not always good philologists, and some of the invented names are crude barbarisms.

Outstanding though Linnæus's services were to systematic nomenclature, it must not be imagined that, as by a wave of a magic wand, he dispelled confusion irrevocably and inaugurated an era of everlasting order. Confusion gradually crept in again, and finally became so rampant that once more it had to be dealt with radically.

In 1889, in Paris, there met a body that received the name of the International Zoölogical Congress. This was the first of a regular series of meetings, and the most recent was held in 1948, also in Paris. The object of these meetings has been to establish and revise from time to time a code of nomenclature for acceptance universally.

One of the most important canons laid down by the Congress is the law of priority. As a starting-point, the Congress have taken the publication in 1758 of the tenth edition of Linnæus's *Systema Naturæ*. After that date the name that was first duly bestowed on any kind of bird takes precedence of all later ones. To originate a name, the would-be author must publish "the name in connection with an indication, a definition, or a description." Sound though the law of priority is in general, its too rigid application has caused trouble, a well-established name, for instance, having had on occasion to give way to one that had been buried in oblivion. It is immaterial whether the name thus unearthed is appropriate or not. "A generic or a specific name," we read, "once published cannot be rejected, even by its author, because of inappropriateness." Thus the song-thrush's expressive specific name of *philomelus* (music-loving) has recently been changed to the fallacious one of *ericetorum* (of the heaths), on the ground that the latter is "the earliest valid name" (Witherby). But, though the earliest, the name is none the less absurd, especially in the light of how it came to be invented. The trouble started in 1796, when Lewin, the bird-artist, figured a bird which really had the appearance of a song-thrush, but which he, under a false impression, labelled the "heath thrush." Eleven years later Turton, the ornithologist, blindly following Lewin in his error, bestowed the name of *ericetorum* on the subject of the figure. Yet, having once been given, the name has now become irrevocable.

It will be gathered then that bird nomenclature still falls far short of the ideal.

ANALYSIS OF GENERIC NAMES

So much for the origin of scientific names. The next step is to elucidate the principles on which they have been formed. Generic names differ fundamentally from specific and sub-specific ones, and should therefore be examined separately. One essential difference between the two classes is that generic names are nouns, whereas specific and sub-specific names are mostly adjectives or quasi-adjectives. A few specific names, however, as has been seen, are nouns, and these will be treated as generic names for our present purpose.

Generic names relate, for the most part, to different aspects of the bird denoted; and these aspects will best serve as the main basis for analysis. Roughly speaking, there are six such aspects: (1) appearance, (2) call, (3) habitat, (4) food, (5) behaviour, (6) legendary association. There are also a few generic names that may be called commemorative.

APPEARANCE

This, as might be expected, is the largest class of all. Thus the redstart is called *Phœnīcūrus*, "crimson-tailed"; and the oyster-catcher *Hæmatopus*, "having blood-red feet."

CALL

This, too, is a large class, which is only natural for a characteristic of such distinction. Some of the names falling in this class are obviously imitative of the bird's call: e.g. *Crex*, crake, and *Corvus*, crow. There is, however, a tendency to overstress this relationship, and to suggest a resemblance between a bird's call and its name, whenever no other explanation is forthcoming. Can we, for instance, agree with Gesner that the lesser whitethroat's call resembles *currūca*? Or with Varro that the swallow's call resembles *hirundo*? Other names that refer to a bird's call make no claim to be imitative. Thus the grasshopper-warbler is named *Lōcustella*, "the little locust-(bird)," because of a supposed resemblance between the bird's call and the insect's chirrup; and the snipe has received the name *Capella*, "the little goat-(bird)," from the resemblance of one of its nuptial calls to a goat's bleating.

HABITAT

Many names refer to a bird's habitat, that is to say, the kind of place where the bird is often found. Thus the sand-martin is called *Rīpāria*, "the bank-(bird)," because of the place where it nests; and some kinds of warbler bear the name *Agrobatēs*, "field-haunting," because they breed chiefly in cultivated land.

FOOD

A few names refer to a bird's favourite kind of food. Thus *Muscicapa* is the exact equivalent of the common name, *flycatcher*; and *Carduēlis*, finch, means literally "the thistle-(bird)."

BEHAVIOUR

A fair number of names are derived from the bird's behaviour. Thus the wagtail is called *Motacilla*, "the little (tail-) mover"; and the shrike is dubbed *Lanius*, "the butcher."

LEGENDARY ASSOCIATION

A few names are derived from legendary persons who, according to classical mythology, were transformed into birds. Thus the sparrow-hawk was called *Nīsus* after a Greek chieftain of that name; and the black-browed albatross was called *Diomēdea* after the companions of the Greek warrior, Diomedes.

COMMEMORATIVE

These names commemorate some person, usually connected with the discovery of a bird: e.g. *Bartramia* (a kind of sandpiper) after Bartram, the American naturalist; *Bulweria* (a kind of petrel) after Bulwer, who provided the typical specimen.

ANALYSIS OF SPECIFIC AND SUB-SPECIFIC NAMES

Broadly speaking, specific and sub-specific names may be divided into five classes—(1) Descriptive names, (2) Names relating to habit, (3) Names relating to place, (4) Commemorative names, (5) Names relating to classification.

DESCRIPTIVE NAMES

These may relate either to a bird's appearance or to its call.

APPEARANCE. This is the largest class of all; and the names may be based on a bird's colour, size or any other visual quality: e.g. *roseus*, rose-coloured, in *Pastor roseus*, rose-coloured starling; *minūtus*, little, in *Ixobrӯchus minutus minutus*, little bittern; *clypeāta*, shield-bearing, in *Spatula clypeata*, shoveler.

CALL. For instance, *modulāris*, warbling, in *Prūnella modularis modularis*, continental hedge-sparrow; *strepera*, rattling, in *Anas strepera*, gadwall.

NAMES RELATING TO HABIT

A large proportion of these names refer to a bird's food: e.g. *glandārius*, acorn-, in *Garrulus glandarius glandarius*, continental jay; *apivorus*, bee-eating, in *Pernis apivorus apivorus*, honey-buzzard. Other habits, however, are sometimes referred to: e.g. *excubitor*, sentinel, in *Lanius excubitor excubitor*, great grey shrike; *gregāria*, sociable, in *Chettūsia gregaria*, sociable plover.

NAMES RELATING TO PLACE

Some of these names refer to the region where a bird is found: e.g. *zetlandicus*, Shetland-, in *Sturnus zetlandicus zetlandicus*, Shetland starling;

arcticus, arctic, in *Colymbus arcticus arcticus*, black-throated diver. Other names in this class refer to the kind of place favoured by a bird: e.g. *domesticus*, house-, in *Passer domesticus domesticus*, house-sparrow; *scirpāceus*, reed-, in *Acrocephalus scirpaceus scirpaceus*, reed-warbler.

COMMEMORATIVE NAMES

A good many names commemorate some person, frequently the person who discovered the bird in question: e.g. *sabīni*, Sabine's, in *Xema sabini*, Sabine's gull; *richardi*, Richard's, in *Anthus richardi richardi*, Richard's pipit.

NAMES RELATING TO CLASSIFICATION

This class contains miscellaneous kinds of names as shown in the following sub-headings.

NAMES EQUIVALENT TO "COMMON." For instance, *commūnis* in *Sylvia communis communis*, white-throat; *triviālis* in *Anthus trivialis trivialis*, tree-pipit.

NAMES RELATING TO THE STATUS OF A SPECIES OR SUB-SPECIES. For instance, *intermedia*, between (two species or sub-species), in *Porzāna pusilla intermedia*, Baillon's crake; *dubius*, doubtful (whether a separate species), in *Charadrius dubius cūronīcus*, little ringed plover.

NAMES INDICATING A RESEMBLANCE TO ANOTHER BIRD. Such names may be either an adjective: e.g. *luscinioidēs*, nightingale-like, in *Lōcustella luscinioides luscinioides*, Savi's warbler; or a noun: e.g. *calandra*, the Greek name for a kind of lark, in *Emberīza calandra*, corn-bunting.

THE FORM OF COMMON NAMES

As we have already seen, not all common names fall within the category of "popular"; many of them are merely book names. A book name, as a rule, consists of a popular name preceded by an adjective or quasi-adjective. Thus *stint* and *brent goose* are popular names, but *Temminck's stint* and *dark-breasted brent goose* are book names. It will be seen, therefore, that popular names are more general than book names.

ORIGIN OF COMMON NAMES

For the purpose of this section we may ignore book names, and confine our attention to the popular ones.

As might be expected, the names of most of our familiar birds have an Anglo-Saxon origin. Thus *dove, finch, hawk, lark, owl, rook, sparrow, starling, swallow, thrush, wren*, all come from this source.

The next most prolific source is French. Many of the names derived from this language were introduced by the Normans, particularly those of game-birds, such as *pheasant, partridge, plover, quail* and *pigeon*. Even now a sportsman shoots, not the Anglo-Saxon dove, but the Norman pigeon; and Norman sportsmen brought with them not merely a taste for falconry, but also the falcon's name.

The Scandinavian languages, too, have made their contribution: e.g. Icelandic *eider*, Swedish *auk*, and Danish *tern*. So, too, have the Celtic languages: e.g. Gaelic *ptarmigan* and *capercaillie*, and Welsh *coot*. Nor does this exhaust the list of languages, but no other has contributed enough to deserve special mention here.

ANALYSIS OF COMMON NAMES

Here too, with the exception of one class of names, it will be appropriate to confine our attention to the popular names. These can conveniently be divided into five classes: that is to say, names relating to a bird's (1) appearance, (2) call, (3) habitat, (4) food, (5) behaviour. For book names a sixth class has to be added—that of commemorative names.

APPEARANCE

For popular names, too, this is the largest class: e.g. *bullfinch, goldcrest, jay, blackcap, spoonbill.*

CALL

Kittiwake, nightjar, whooper swan.

HABITAT

Fieldfare, wood-lark, stock-dove.

FOOD

Chaffinch, goshawk, herring-gull, mistle-thrush.

BEHAVIOUR

Dipper, swift, wryneck.

COMMEMORATIVE

A fair number of book names commemorate persons connected with the discovery of a bird, as was the case with scientific names. For instance, *Tengmalm's owl* is called after the Swedish ornithologist, and *White's thrush* after Gilbert White of Selborne.

LIST OF ANCIENT AUTHORITIES TO WHOM REFERENCE IS MADE IN THE LISTS OF SCIENTIFIC AND COMMON NAMES

1. ÆLIAN. Author of *On the Nature of Animals*. A Roman who wrote in Greek. Flourished at the beginning of the third century A.D.

2. ANTŌNĪNUS LĪBERĀLIS. Author of a collection of tales of mythical transformations, in Greek. Flourished probably about A.D. 150.

3. APPULEIUS. Author of *The Golden Ass*, in Latin. Born at Madaura in N.E. Africa about A.D. 124.

4. ARISTOPHANĒS. Famous author of comic Greek plays, including *The Birds*. Born about 444 B.C., probably at Athens.

5. ARISTOTLE. See page 7.

6. ATHĒNÆUS. Author of *The Banquet of the Learned*, in Greek. Born at Naucratis in Egypt. Flourished about the end of the second and beginning of the third century A.D.

7. *Carmen dē Philomēlā* (The Song about the Nightingale). Author unknown. Written about A.D. 500.

8. CICERO. Famous Roman orator and statesman, 106–43 B.C. Author of *On the Nature of the Gods* and *On Divination*, including augury from birds.

9. DIOGENĒS LAËRTIUS. Author of *Lives of the Philosophers*, in Greek. Born at Laerte in Cilicia, Asia Minor. Lived probably in the second century A.D.

10. FESTUS. Roman grammarian of the fourth century A.D. Author of a Latin dictionary.

11. HERODOTUS. Famous Greek historian. "Father of History." Born at Halicarnassus in Caria, Asia Minor, in 484 B.C.

12. HESYCHIUS. Author of a Greek dictionary. Born at Alexandria in the fourth century A.D.

13. HOMER. The great epic poet of Greece. Author of the *Iliad* and *Odyssey*. Flourished perhaps about 850 B.C.

14. JUVENAL. Famous Roman satirist. Flourished towards the close of the first century A.D.

15. MARTIAL. Latin epigrammatic poet. Born at Bilbilis in Spain about A.D. 40, died about A.D. 104.

16. OPPIAN. Author of the Greek poem *Ixeutika* (Bird-catching). Lived probably in the second or third century A.D.

17. OVID. Famous Roman poet, 43 B.C.–A.D. 18. Author of *Metamorphosēs* (Transformations).

18. PLAUTUS. Famous author of comic Latin plays. Born about 254 B.C.
19. PLINY. See page 7.
20. SERVIUS. Latin grammarian of the fourth or fifth century A.D.
21. VARRO. Roman writer, known as "the most learned of the Romans," 116–28 B.C. Author of *Dē Rē Rusticā* (On Country Matters) and *Dē Linguā Latīnā* (On the Latin Language).
22. VIRGIL. Famous Roman poet, 70–19 B.C. Author of the *Ænēid* and *Georgics*.

LIST OF MEDIEVAL AND MODERN AUTHORITIES
TO WHOM REFERENCE IS MADE IN THE LISTS
OF SCIENTIFIC AND COMMON NAMES

(This list does not include the name of any person who is mentioned merely as the author of a scientific name or who is sufficiently described in the context where he is mentioned.)

1. ALBERTUS MAGNUS. See page 7.
2. ALBIN. British bird-artist. Flourished about 1750.
3. ALDROVANDUS. Italian naturalist, 1522–1605.
4. BELON. French naturalist, 1517–1564.
5. BILLBERG. German ornithologist. Author of *Synopsis Faunæ Scandināviæ* (1828).
6. BLYTH, EDWARD. British ornithologist, 1810–1873.
7. BONELLI. Italian physician and naturalist, 1784–1830.
8. CAMDEN. English antiquary and historian, 1551–1623.
9. CHARLETON. English naturalist, 1619–1707.
10. DRAYTON. English poet, 1563–1631.
11. FORSTER. British naturalist. Accompanied Captain Cook in his voyages in the second half of the eighteenth century.
12. GAZA. See page 7.
13. GESNER. See page 7.
14. KUHL. German naturalist, 1797–1821.
15. LATHAM. British ornithologist, 1740–1837.
16. LESSON. French naturalist and antiquary, 1794–1849
17. LINNÆUS. See pages 6, 7, 8.
18. LITTRÉ. Author of a great French dictionary, 1801–1881.
19. LUBBOCK. English naturalist, 1798–1876.
20. NEWTON. English ornithologist, 1829–1907.
21. PALLAS. German naturalist and traveller, 1741–1811.
22. PENNANT. British naturalist, 1726–1798.
23. RAY. "Father of English Natural History," 1628–1705.
24. SABINE, JOSEPH. British naturalist, 1770–1837.
25. SAVI. Italian geologist and ornithologist, 1798–1871.
26. SCHLEGEL. German naturalist, 1804–1884.
27. SCOPOLI. Italian naturalist and chemist, 1723–1788.
28. STEJNEGER. American ornithologist. Part author of the *Standard Natural History* (1885).
29. TURNER, WILLIAM. English naturalist, 1500–1568.
30. WILLUGHBY. English naturalist, 1635–1672.

ABBREVIATIONS

adj., adjective
A.-S., Anglo-Saxon
cf., compare
dim., diminutive
E., English
fem., feminine
Fr., French
gen., genitive
Gr., Greek
L., Latin
lit., literally
M., medieval (language)
O., old (language)
part., participle
pres. part., present participle
ref., reference

LIST I: SCIENTIFIC NAMES

Accipiter Brisson. L. *accipiter*, hawk (Pliny, X, 9); *accipio*, seize; *ad*, towards, and *capio*, take; with ref. to the bird's predatory habit. A difficulty about this derivation is that the usual meaning of *accipio* in classical L. is not "seize," but "receive." However, in M.L. *accipio* undoubtedly means "seize"; for Albertus Magnus, with regard to one kind of *accipiter*, says "magnas aves accipit," which evidently means "it seizes large birds." **A. gentīlis ātricapillus** (Wilson), American goshawk. *Gentilis*, see below. *Atricapillus*, L., black-haired; *ater* (gen. *atri*), black, and *capillus*, hair of the head; from the bird's nearly black crown. **A. gentīlis gentilis** (Linnæus), goshawk. M.L. *gentilis*, noble; with ref. to its prowess at hunting in the days of falconry. Albertus Magnus describes this bird as "the most noble kind of all falcons" (genus falconum nobilissimum), with obvious ref. to this characteristic. It used to be known as "the gentle falcon," "gentle" here corresponding to *gentilis*. **A. nīsus nisus** (Linnæus), sparrow-hawk. M.L. *nisus*, sparrow-hawk; after Nisus, a king of Megara (in Ancient Greece), who was said to have been changed into a sea-eagle (Ovid: *Metamorphosēs*, VIII, 146).

Acrocephalus Naumann. "Pointed-headed"; coined from Gr. *akros*, apparently here taken to mean "pointed," though its true meaning is "at the point," and *kephalē*, head. **A. agricola agricola** (Jerdon), paddy-field warbler. L. *agricola*, farmer; from its habit of frequenting cultivated (paddy-) fields in India, where the typical specimen was found. **A. arundināceus arundinaceus** (Linnæus), great reed-warbler. L. *arundinaceus*, here meaning "of the reeds," though its original meaning is "reed-like"; *arundo* (gen. *arundinis*), reed; from the bird's habitat. **A. arundināceus orientālis** (Temminck and Schlegel), eastern great reed-warbler. *Arundinaceus*, see above. *Orientalis*, L., eastern; breeds in E. Asia. **A. dūmētōrum** Blyth, Blyth's reed-warbler. "Of the thickets"; gen. plural of L. *dumetum;* from the bird's partiality for this kind of habitat, though it also frequents marshy ground. **A. palūdicola** (Vieillot), aquatic warbler. L. *paludicola*, marsh-dweller; *palus* (gen. *paludis*), marsh, and *colo*, inhabit; the bird frequents marshes in both summer and winter. **A. palustris** (Bechstein), marsh-warbler. L. *palustris*, marsh-; *palus*, marsh; the bird is usually found near water, but sometimes on quite dry land. **A. schœnobænus** (Linnæus), sedge-warbler. "Rush-haunter"; coined from Gr. *skhoinos*, rush, and *baino*, go; with ref. to the bird's favourite habitat in summer. **A. scirpāceus scirpaceus** (Hermann), reed-warbler. Adj. coined from L. *scirpus*, reed; with ref. to the bird's favourite habitat, especially in summer.

Actitis Illiger. Gr. *aktitēs*, dweller on the coast; *aktē*, coast; these birds are found both on the coast and near inland water. **A. hypoleucos** (Linnæus), common sandpiper. Gr. *hupoleukos*, which originally meant "whitish," from prefix *hupo-*, somewhat, and *leukos*, white; but which here apparently means "white underneath," *hupo* being used in the prepositional sense of "under." **A. maculāria** (Linnæus), spotted sandpiper. Fem. adj. coined from L. *macula*, a spot; the adults have black spots on their under parts in summer.

Ægithalos Hermann. Gr. *aigithalos*, a kind of tit mentioned by Aristotle (616b, 3); derivation unknown. **A. caudātus caudatus** (Linnæus), northern long-tailed tit. M.L. *caudatus*, having a (large) tail; L. *cauda*, tail; the bird's tail is much longer than its wings. **A. caudātus rosāceus** Mathews, British long-tailed tit. *Caudatus*, see above. *Rosaceus*, L., meaning originally "made of roses," but here "rose-coloured"; from the bird's pink markings. **Ægolius** Kaup. Gr. *aigolios*, a kind of owl (Aristotle 592b, 11); derivation unknown. **A. fūnereus funereus** (Linnæus),

17

Tengmalm's owl. L. *funereus*, ill-boding; *funus* (gen. *funeris*), funeral, death, ruin; *funebris*, which also means ill-boding, is applied by Pliny (X, 16) to the kind of owl that he calls *būbo;* but there is no reason to identify this with Tengmalm's owl.

Agrobatēs Swainson. Gr. *agrobates*, haunting the fields; *agros*, field, and *baino*, go; these birds breed chiefly in cultivated land. **A. galactōtēs galactotes** (Temminck), rufous warbler. Mistake for *galactodes*, which is Gr. for "milk-white"; *gala* (gen. *galaktos*), milk, and *eidos*, form, appearance; with ref. to the white tips of the bird's tail feathers, except the central ones. **A. galactōtēs syriacus** (Hemprich and Ehrenberg), brown-backed warbler. *Galactotes*; see above. *Syriacus*, L., Syrian; the typical specimen was found in Syria, but the bird also breeds in Asia Minor and the Balkan peninsula.

Alauda Linnæus. L. *alauda* (Pliny, XI, 44), lark; Pliny tells us that the word is Celtic; the meaning apparently is "great songstress"; cf. Welsh *al*, great, and *awd,* song. **A. arvensis arvensis** Linnæus, sky-lark. L. *arvensis*, of the cultivated field; *arvum*, cultivated field; frequents cultivated fields and grassland. **A. arvensis intermedia** Swinhoe, eastern sky-lark. *Arvensis*, see above. *Intermedia*, fem. of L. *intermedius*, intermediate; that is, between *Alauda pekinensis* and *Alauda cœlivox*.

Alca Linnæus. Latinized form of Swedish *alka*, auk. **A. impennis** Linnæus, great auk. "Wingless"; coined from L. prefix *im-*, without, and *pennæ*, wing (plural of *penna*, feather); this extinct bird had wings, but they were too short to fly with. **A. torda britannica** Ticehurst, British razorbill. *Torda*, see below. *Britannica*, fem. of L. *Britannicus*, British; breeds mainly in the British Isles. **A. torda torda** Linnæus, northern razorbill. *Torda* is the name by which the bird is known in the Gottland province of Sweden; cf. the general Swedish name, *tordmule*.

Alcēdo Linnæus. (H)*alcedo*, kingfisher (Varro), L. form of Gr. (*h*)*alkuon*; after (H)alcyone, who was the daughter of Æolus, god of the winds, the Greek legend being that she was turned into the bird that afterwards bore her name (Ovid; *Metamorphosēs*, XI, 742–6). **A. atthis ispida** Linnæus. *Atthis*, Gr., Athenian (woman); possibly Linnæus, when applying this name to the kingfisher, had in mind the legend (see under **Alcedo** above) that the bird was a transformed Greek (if not Athenian) woman, in the same way as the Latin poet Martial (I, 53, 9 and V, 67, 2) had applied the name to the nightingale and swallow on account of similar transformations. The application of *atthis* to this kingfisher is, however, artificial; Linnæus's original name for the bird was *Alcedo ispida*, but because, six pages earlier, he had given the name of *Gracula atthis* to a similar Egyptian bird, it has been decreed by modern ornithologists that *atthis* should be assumed as the (European) kingfisher's specific title and that *ispida* should be relegated to subspecific status. *Ispida*, variation of *hispida*, the name mentioned by Albertus Magnus; Gesner cites authority for holding that the name is imitative of the bird's call, but this is difficult to understand.

Alectoris Kaup. Gr. *alektoris*, domestic hen (Aristotle, 558b, 18); fem. of *alektor*, poetic form of *alektruon*. The appropriateness of the name for this genus is not clear. **A. rūfa rufa** (Linnæus), red-legged partridge. Fem. of L. *rufus*, red; with ref. to its legs and bill and the patch round its eyes.

Alle Link. The name used for a sea-bird in Œland Island, Sweden. **A. alle alle** (Linnæus), little auk.

Anas Linnæus. L. *anas*, a duck; from *no* (root *na*), swim (Varro). **A. acūta acuta** Linnæus, pintail. Fem. of L. *acutus*, sharp, pointed; with ref. to its tail. **A. americāna** Gmelin, American wigeon. Coined fem. adj.; breeds in N. America, winters mostly in N. and Central America. **A. crecca carolinensis** Gmelin, green-winged teal. *Crecca*, see below. Carolinensis, of Carolina, U.S.A., where the typical specimen was found; but the bird is found in many parts of N. and Central America. **A. crecca crecca** Linnæus, teal. *Crecca*, a coined word; probably represents the sound of the bird's incessant calling; cf. the onomatopœic Gr. word, *kreko*, cause a string to sound by striking it. **A. discors** Linnæus, blue-winged teal. L. *discors*; the original meaning is "disagreeing," but here apparently the word is taken to mean "harsh," with ref. to the bird's call. **A. pēnelopē** Linnæus, wigeon. Gr. *penelops* (Aristotle, 593b, 25), a kind of sea-bird.

According to Gesner, the bird was called after Penelope who became the wife of Ulysses; the legend being that, when a baby, she was thrown into the sea by her parents, but rescued by birds that in consequence received her name. It is, however, more probable that the legend arose from the name of the bird, and that the real origin of the name is unknown. **A. platyrhyncha platyrhyncha** Linnæus, mallard. Latinized fem. of Gr. *platurrhunkhos*, broad-billed; *platus*, broad, and *rhunkhos*, bill. **A. querquedula** Linnæus, garganey. L. *querquedula*, a kind of duck; derived from Gr. (Varro); perhaps a L. fem. dim. form of Gr. *krex* (gen. *krekos*), a bird with a call sounding like its name; *krex* comes from *kreko*, cause a string to sound by striking it. For the use of the suffix -*ulus* to form a dim. cf. *homunculus*, little man, from *homo* (gen. *hominis*), man. **A. strepera** Linnæus, gadwall. Fem. adj. coined from L. *strepo*, to rattle; with ref. to its call.

Anser Brisson. L. *anser*, goose; according to Varro, imitative of the bird's call; cognate with E. *gander*. **A. albifrons albifrons** (Scopoli), white-fronted goose. Coined from L. *albus* (gen. *albi*), white, and *frons*, forehead; with ref. to the white patch at the base of the bird's bill in front of its head. **A. anser anser** (Linnæus), grey lag-goose. **A. erythropus** (Linnæus), lesser white-fronted goose. Gr. *eruthropous*, red-footed; *eruthros*, red, and *pous*, foot. **A. fabālis brachyrhynchus** Baillon, pink-footed goose. *Fabalis*, see below. *Brachyrhynchus*,

short-billed; coined from Gr. *brakhus*, short, and *rhunkhos*, bill. **A. fabālis fabalis** (Latham), bean-goose. L. *fabalis*, bean-; *faba*, bean; the implication being that the bird is specially partial to beans, but this is not really so. **A. hyperboreus atlanticus** (Kennard), greater snow-goose. *Hyperboreus*, see below. *Atlanticus*, atlantic; found mainly on the east coast of N. America. **A. hyperboreus hyperboreus** Pallas, snow-goose. Gr. *huperboreos*, of the extreme north, arctic; lit. "beyond the north wind"; *huper*, beyond, and *Boreas*, (personified) North Wind; breeds in the arctic region.

Anthus Bechstein. Gr. *anthos*, name of a bird mentioned by Aristotle (609b, 14). According to a Greek legend, Anthus was a youth who was killed by his father's horses and then changed into the bird that received its name from him (Antōnīnus Līberālis: *Transformations*, VII); but the youth may well have been called after the bird and not the bird after the youth. Gesner, indeed, says that the bird's name means "flowery," as though from Gr. *anthos*, a flower; but why the bird should be called "flowery" is not clear. **A. campestris campestris** (Linnæus), tawny pipit. L. *campestris*, of the open field; *campus*, an open field. **A. cervīnus** (Pallas), red-throated pipit. "Stag-like," "tawny"; coined from L. *cervus*, stag; with ref. to the bird's reddish throat and breast in spring and summer. **A. gustāvi** Swinhoe, Petchora pipit. Named in 1863 after the German ornithologist, Gustavus Schlegel, who discovered the bird at Amoy, China. **A. prātensis** (Linnæus), meadow-pipit. L. *pratensis*, meadow-; *pratum*, meadow; found only in open country. **A. richardi** Vieillot, Richard's pipit. After M. Richard of Luneville, who sent the first specimens to Vieillot from Lorraine in 1815. **A. spīnoletta littorālis** Brehm, Scandinavian rock-pipit. *Spinoletta*, see under *A. spinoletta spinoletta*. *Littoralis*, L., of the coast; *lit(i)us* (gen. *litoris*), coast. **A. spīnoletta meinertzhägeni** E. G. Bird, Hebridean rock-pipit. *Spinoletta*, see under *A. spinoletta spinoletta*. *Meinertzhageni*, after the British ornithologist, Colonel R. Meinertzhagen, who noted the occurrence of this form in 1934. **A. spinoletta petrōsus** (Montagu), rock-pipit. *Spinoletta*, see under *A. spinoletta spinoletta*. *Petrosus*, L., originally meaning "rocky," but here "of the rock"; Gr. *petra*, rock; breeds mainly on rocky coasts and islands. **A. spinoletta rubescens** (Tunstall), American water-pipit. *Spinoletta*, see under *A. spinoletta spinoletta*. *Rubescens*, L., reddish; pres. part. of *rubesco*, grow red; from the colour of the bird's under parts. **A. spinoletta spinoletta** (Linnæus), water-pipit. *Spinoletta*, a mistake for *spipoletta*, dim. of Italian *spipola*, titlark. *Spipola* itself is imitative of the bird's twittering. **A. triviālis trivialis** (Linnæus), tree-pipit. L. *trivialis*, common; lit. "of the road-junction," that is, "of a public place"; prefix *tri-*, three, and *via*, road.

Apus Scopoli. Gr. *apous*, a swift (Aristotle 487b, 25); lit. "footless," from prefix *a-*, without, and *pous*, foot; with ref. to the shortness of the bird's feet, which are useless for moving on the ground. **A. apus apus** (Linnæus), swift. **A. melba melba** (Linnæus), Alpine swift. Old German name for a gull (Albertus Magnus); what resemblance Linnæus saw between the Alpine swift and a gull is not clear—possibly the ref. is to the Alpine swift's breeding, among other places, in cliffs. *Melba* is cognate with E. *mew*, both names being imitative of the bird's call.

Aquila Brisson. L. *aquila*, eagle. According to Festus, fem. of *aquilus*, dark; *aquilus* itself being derived from *aqua*, water. Albertus Magnus, however, connects the word with *acūmen*, keenness; with ref. to the bird's keen sight, keen spirit, and keen talons and bill. **A. chrȳsaëtus chrysaetus** (Linnæus), golden eagle. Gr. *khrusaetos*, golden eagle (Ælian, II, 39); *khrusos*, gold, and *aetos*, eagle; from the colour of its head, neck and feet. **A. clanga** Pallas, spotted eagle. L. *clanga*, a kind of eagle (Pliny, X, 3), though some texts have

plangus instead; probably from *clangor*, a scream, with ref. to the bird's call.

Ardea Linnæus. L. *ardea*, heron (Virgil: *Georgics*, I, 364); Gr. *erodios*, heron. **A. cinerea cinerea** Linnæus, common heron. Fem. of L. *cinereus*, ash-coloured; *cinis* (gen. *cineris*), ashes; with ref. to the bird's upper parts and tail. **A. purpurea purpurea** Linnæus, purple heron. Fem. of L. *purpureus*, purple; its crown and crest are purplish black and its breast purplish red.

Ardeola Boie. Coined dim. of L. *ardea*, heron. **A. ībis ibis** (Linnæus), buff-backed heron. L. *ibis*, ibis (Pliny, X, 45); originally the name had nothing to do with a heron. **A. ralloidēs** (Scopoli), squacco heron. "Rail-like"; coined from *rallus*, the latinized form of Fr. *râle*, rail (bird), and Gr. *eidos*, form, appearance.

Arēnāria Brisson. Fem. of L. *arenarius*, sand-; *arena*, sand. The turnstone is found mainly on rocky and pebbly shores, but, outside the breeding-season, on sandy flats as well. **A. interpres interpres** (Linnæus), turnstone. L. *interpres*, usually meaning "interpreter" or "go-between," but here apparently "telltale," with ref. to the alarm note with which it warns other birds of the approach of danger.

Asio Brisson. L. *asio*, long-eared owl (Pliny, X, 33). **A. flammeus flammeus** Pontoppidan, short-eared owl. L. *flammeus*, flame-coloured; *flamma*, flame; the bird's general colour is really dark buff. **A. ōtus otus** (Linnæus), long-eared owl. Gr. *otos*, long-eared owl; *ous* (gen. *otos*), ear.

Athēnē Boie. After the Greek goddess Athene (called Minerva by the Romans), with whom an owl was associated. **A. noctua vidalii** A. E. Brehm. *Noctua*, L., a kind of night-owl (Pliny, X, 19); *nox* (gen. *noctis*), night; with ref. to its habit of hunting by night. *Vidalii*, after Ignatius Vidal, who was director of the Zoölogical Museum at Valencia, Spain, when the bird received its name (1857).

Aythya Boie. Gr. *aithuia*, diver (water-bird), (Aristotle, 487a, 23). **A. ferīna** (Linnæus), common pochard. Fem. of L. *ferinus*, game-; *ferus*, wild (animal); the bird was used as meat. **A. fūlīgula** (Linnæus), tufted duck. Coined fem. dim. of L. *fuligo*, soot; with ref. to the male's black head, breast and back. **A. marīla marila** (Linnæus), scaup-duck. Gr. *marīlē*, charcoal embers; with ref. to the male's black head, shoulders, breast and tail. **A. nyroca nyroca** (Güldenstädt), ferruginous duck. Russian *nyrok*, a kind of water-bird.

Bartramia Lesson. After the traveller and naturalist, William Bartram of Philadelphia (1739–1823), near whose botanic garden by the river Schuykill (Pennsylvania) the bird was first found by Lesson. **B. longicauda** (Bechstein), Bartram's sandpiper. "Long-tailed"; fem. adj. coined from L. *longus* (gen. *longi*) and *cauda*, tail.

Bombycilla Vieillot. "Silk-tail"; coined from Gr. *bombux* (gen. *bombūkos*), silkworm, silk, and a supposed L. word *cilla*, tail; with ref. to the bright-yellow tip of the bird's tail. For the origin of the error about *cilla* see under *Mōtacilla*. **B. garrulus garrulus** (Linnæus), waxwing. *Garrulus* here means "jay-like," *garrulus* being the name of the genus to which the jay belongs. In classical L. *garrulus* meant "talkative," which is a suitable name for the jay, but not for the waxwing, which is rather silent.

Botaurus Stephens. Latinized form of M.E. *botor* or Fr. *butor*, which may come from L. *būteo*, though *buteo* (Pliny, X, 9) is believed to have meant "buzzard"; the M.E. and Fr. names are probably imitative of the bird's booming call. Possibly, however, *Botaurus* was also intended to suggest a derivation from the two old L. words *bos*, ox, and *taurus*, bull; in allusion to the bittern's old L. name *taurus*, which according to Pliny (X, 57) had its origin in the bird's imitating a bull's bellowing. **B. lentiginōsus** (Montagu), American bittern. L. *lentiginosus*, freckled; *lentigo* (gen.

lentiginis), lentil-shaped spot, freckle; with ref. to the bird's speckled upper parts. **B. stellāris stellaris** (Linnæus), bittern. L. *stellaris*, meaning originally "starry," but here "starred," "mottled"; with ref. to its mottled plumage.

Branta Scopoli. Probably latinized form of some name cognate with E. *brent*; see under "Goose, Brent" in List II. **B. bernicla bernicla** (Linnæus), dark-breasted brent goose. Latinized form of *barnacle*; see under "Goose, Barnacle" in List II. **B. bernicla hrota** (Müller), pale-breasted brent goose. *Bernicla*, see above. *Hrota*, Icelandic *hrot-gaes*, barnacle-goose; from *hrota*, snoring; with ref. to the bird's snore-like call. **B. canadensis canadensis** (Linnæus), Canada goose. A coined word; the bird breeds in Canada and the northern part of the U.S.A. **B. leucopsis** (Bechstein), barnacle-goose. "White-faced"; coined from Gr. *leukos*, white, and *opsis*, face. **B. rūficollis** (Pallas), red-breasted goose. "Red-necked"; coined from L. *rufus*, red, and *collum*, neck; the bird's neck and upper breast are both chestnut.

Būbo Duméril. L. *bubo*, eagle-owl (Pliny, X, 16); cognate with Gr. *buas* (Aristotle, 592b, 9), eagle-owl, from *buzo*, to hoot. **B. bubo bubo** (Linnæus), eagle-owl.

Bucephala Baird. Gr. *boukephalos*, ox-headed; *bous*, ox, and *kephalē*, head; with ref. to the squatness of the bird's head. **B. albeola** (Linnæus), buffel-headed duck. Coined fem. dim. of L. *albus*, white; from the white patch behind its eye. **B. clangula clangula** (Linnæus), golden-eye. Fem. dim. adj. coined from L. *clango*, to clang; with ref. to the noise that its wings make in flight.

Bulweria Bonaparte. After Bulwer, whose petrel from Madeira was used by Jardine and Selby for their *Illustrations of Ornithology* (1828). **B. bulwerii** (Jardine and Selby), Bulwer's petrel.

Burhīnus Illiger. "Ox-nosed"; should be spelt *burrhinus*; coined from Gr. *bous*, ox, and *rhis* (*rhinos*), nose; with ref. to the squatness of the bird's bill. **B. œdicnēmus œdicnemus** (Linnæus), stone-curlew. "Swollen-shinned"; coined from Gr. *oideo*, to swell (intransitive), and *knēmē*, shin; with ref. to the appearance of the young bird's tarsi. **Būteo** Lacépède. L. *buteo*, buzzard (Pliny, X, 9); cognate with Gr. *buzo*, to hoot; though the common buzzard's call is more of a mew. **B. buteo buteo** (Linnæus), common buzzard. **B. buteo vulpīnus** Gloger, steppe-buzzard. *Vulpinus*, L. adj. from *vulpes*, fox; because it preys on fox cubs. **B. lagōpus lagopus** (Pontoppidan), rough-legged buzzard. Gr. *lagopous*, hare-footed; *lagos*, hare, and *pous*, foot; with ref. to the bird's feathered tarsi.

Calandrella Kaup. Coined L. dim. of Gr. *kalandra*, a kind of lark (Oppian: *Ixeutika*, III, 15). **C. brachydactyla brachydactyla** (Leisler), short-toed lark. "Short-toed"; coined from Gr. *brakhus*, short, and *daktulos*, finger, toe; with ref. to the bird's short hind-toe. **C. brachydactyla longipennis** (Eversmann), eastern short-toed lark. *Brachydactyla*, see above. *Longipennis*, long-winged; coined from L. *longus* (gen. *longi*), long, and *pennæ*, wing (plural of *penna*, feather); the ref. seems to be to the long secondaries of the wings of both forms of short-toed lark.

Calcārius Bechstein. L. *calcarius*; the original L. word was derived from *calx* (gen. *calcis*), limestone, but here it is taken to come from *calcar*, a spur, and to mean "spurred"; with ref. to the bird's long hind-claw. **C. lappōnicus lapponicus** (Linnæus), Lapland bunting. A coined word; the typical specimen came from Lapland, but the bird breeds in many other places in or near the arctic region.

Calidris Anonymous. Gr. *(s)kalidris*, a grey, speckled water-bird (Aristotle, 593b, 8). **C. acūmināta** (Horsfield), Siberian pectoral sandpiper. Fem. of L. *acuminatus*, pointed; past part. passive of *acumino*, sharpen; with ref. to the shape of the bird's tail. **C. alpīna alpina**

(Linnæus), northern dunlin. Fem. of L. *alpinus*, alpine; but apparently "alpine" here means "found in an alpine climate," the bird's chief breeding-place being N. Europe. **C. alpīna schinzii** (Brehm), southern dunlin. *Alpina*, see above. *Schinzii*, after the German ornithologist, Heinrich Rudolf Schinz (1777–1861). **C. bairdii** (Coues), Baird's sandpiper. After the American ornithologist, Spencer Fullerton Baird (1823–87). **C. canūtus canutus** (Linnæus), knot. Latinized form of E. *knot*; said to refer to King Canute. The germ of the idea appears in a remark made by Camden (*Britannia*, 1607): "Knotts, i. Canuti aves, ut opinor e Dania enim advolare creduntur" ("Knots, that is, Canute's birds, I suppose, for they are believed to fly here from Denmark"). A different explanation, however, is given by Drayton, who says that knots were brought to England, Canute's "appetite to please" (*Polyolbion*). Others have sought for an explanation in the fact that knots are found on the sea-shore, as Canute was on one famous occasion. But it is doubtful whether the name has anything to do with Canute at all; the knot is also called locally the "gnat" or "gnat snap." **C. fuscicollis** (Vieillot), Bonaparte's sandpiper. "Dark-necked"; coined from L. *fuscus* (gen. *fusci*), dark, and *collum*, neck. **C. maritima maritima** (Brünnich), purple sandpiper. Fem. of L. *maritimus*, sea-; outside the breeding-season the bird is found only near the coast. **C. melanōtos** (Vieillot), American pectoral sandpiper. A barbarously coined word, meaning "black-backed"; Gr. *melas* (gen. *melanos*), black, and *noton*, back; with ref. to the blackish streaks on that part of the bird. **C. minūta** (Leisler), little stint. Fem. of L. *minutus*, little; this bird is one of the smallest species of *Calidris*, being only about 5¾ in. long, compared with the knot's 10 in. **C. minūtilla** (Vieillot), American stint. "Very little"; fem. of *minutillus*, which is a corruption of L. *minutulus*, dim. of *minutus*, little; this bird is only about 5¼ in. long, and therefore smaller even than the little stint. **C. pusilla** (Linnæus), semi-palmated sandpiper. Fem. of L. *pusillus*, petty; this bird is as small as the little stint, being only about 5¾ in. long. **C. temminckii** (Leisler), Temminck's stint. After the Dutch ornithologist, Coenraad Jacob Temminck (1778–1858). **C. testācea** (Pallas), curlew-sandpiper. Fem. of L. *testaceus*; adj. from *testa*, a secondary meaning of which is "shell-fish"; it evidently refers here to the bird's habit of eating shell-fish, but *testaceus* never has such a meaning in classical Latin.

Capella Frenzel. L. *capella*, little she-goat; fem. dim. of *caper*, goat; with ref. to the sound made by the common snipe, particularly the male, in its downward flight during the breeding-season, which has been likened to a goat's bleating; cf. the Scotch name "heather-bleater." **C. gallīnāgo dēlicāta** (Ord), American snipe. *Gallinago*, see under "Capella gallinago gallinago." *Delicata*, fem. of L. *delicatus*, probably meaning here "tender," "tasty"; with ref. to the bird's table qualities. **C. gallīnāgo færœensis** (Brehm), Færoe snipe. *Gallinago*, see below. *Færœensis*, coined word, meaning "of the Færoe Islands"; breeds in the Færoe Islands and Iceland. **C. gallīnāgo gallinago** (Linnæus), common snipe. Coined from *gallina*, domestic hen; why the name should be applied to the snipe is not clear. **C. media** (Latham), great snipe. Fem. of L. *medius*, intermediate; that is, of a size between the woodcock and the common snipe; all three birds belonged to the genus *Scolopax* in Latham's time, their scientific names being respectively: woodcock, *Scolopax rusticola*; great snipe, *Scolopax media*; common snipe, *Scolopax gallīnāgo*.

Caprimulgus Linnæus. L. *caprimulgus*, goat-milker; *caper* (gen. *capri*), goat, and *mulgeo*, to milk; with ref. to a baseless belief that goes back as far as Aristotle (618b, 5). **C. ægyptius ægyptius** Lichtenstein, Egyptian nightjar. L. *Ægyptius*, Egyptian; the typical specimen came from Egypt, but the bird breeds not only in Egypt, but also in Nubia and eastwards to Irak. **C. europæus europæus** Linnæus, nightjar.

L. *Europæus*, European; breeds mainly in Europe. **C. rūficollis dēsertōrum** Erlanger, Algerian red-necked nightjar. *Ruficollis*, red-necked; coined from L. *rufus* (gen. *rufi*), red, and *collum*, neck; with ref. to the bird's yellow-rufous collar. *Desertorum*, of the deserts; gen. plural of L. *desertum*; frequents uncultivated hills.

Carduēlis Brisson. L. *carduelis*, goldfinch (Pliny, X, 57); *carduus*, thistle; with ref. to the bird's favourite food. **C. cannabina cannabina** (Linnæus), linnet. Fem. of L. *cannabinus*, meaning originally "hempen," but here "hemp-eating"; from Gr. *kannabis*, hemp; with ref. to the bird's fondness for the seeds of that plant, though it feeds on many other kinds of seeds as well and also on insects. **C. carduēlis britannica** (Hartert), British goldfinch. *Britannica*, fem. of L. *Britannicus*, British; confined to the British Isles and Channel Islands. **C. carduēlis carduelis** (Linnæus), continental goldfinch. **C. citrinella citrinella** (Pallas), citril finch. Dim. fem. of M.L. *citrinus*, citron-coloured; though the bird's plumage is mostly yellowish-green. **C. flammea cabaret** (P. L. S. Müller), lesser redpoll. *Flammea*, see under *C. flammea flammea*. *Cabaret*, 18th century Fr. name for a kind of finch. **C. flammea flammea** (Linnæus), mealy redpoll. Fem. of L. *flammeus*, flame-coloured; *flamma*, flame; with ref. to the bird's crimson forehead. **C. flammea holboellii** (Brehm), Holböll's redpoll. *Flammea*, see under *C. flammea flammea*. *Holboellii*, after the Danish ornithologist, Holböll (1795–1856). **C. flammea rostrāta** (Coues), Greenland redpoll. *Flammea*, see under *C. flammea flammea*. *Rostrata*, fem. of L. *rostratus*, having a (large) bill; *rostrum*, bill; with ref. to the bulginess of this feature of the bird. **C. flāvirostris flavirostris** (Linnæus), continental twite. "Yellow-billed"; coined from L. *flavus* (gen. *flavi*), yellow, and *rostrum*, bill; with ref. to the bill's colour in winter—in the breeding-season it is greyish. **C. flāvirostris pīpilans** (Latham), British twite. *Flavirostris*, see above. *Pipilans*, pres.

part. of L. *pipilo*, to chirp; the common name expresses the same idea. **C. hornemanni exīlipes** (Coues), Coues's redpoll. *Hornemanni*, see below. *Exilipes*, thin-footed; coined from L. *exilis*, thin, and *pes*, foot. **C. hornemanni hornemanni** (Holböll), Hornemann's redpoll. After the Danish naturalist, Jens Wilken Hornemann (1770–1841). **C. spinus** (Linnæus), siskin. Gr. *spinos*, a kind of finch that was sold for food in Ancient Athens (Aristophanēs; *Birds*, 1079), perhaps the siskin; from *spīzo*, to chirp.

Carpodacus Kaup. "Fruit-biter"; coined from Gr. *karpos*, fruit, and *dakno*, to bite. **C. erythrinus erythrinus** (Pallas), scarlet grosbeak. "Red"; coined from Gr. *eruthros*, red; with ref. to the male's plumage.

Casarca Bonaparte. South Russian name for a goose. **C. ferrūginea** (Pallas), ruddy sheld-duck. Fem. of L. *ferrugineus*, rust-coloured; *ferrugo* (gen. *ferruginis*), iron-rust; *ferrum*, iron; with ref. to the bird's prevailing colour.

Certhia Linnæus. Gr. *kerthios*, tree-creeper (Aristotle, 616b, 28). **C. familiāris britannica** Ridgway, British tree-creeper. *Familiaris*, see below. *Britannica*, fem. of L. *Britannicus*, British; confined to the British Isles. **C. familiāris familiaris** Linnæus, northern tree-creeper. L. *familiaris*, adj. from *familia*, family; its original meaning is "domestic," "friendly," but here it probably means "living in family-fashion"; with ref. to the birds' habit of forming small parties.

Cettia Bonaparte. After the Italian Jesuit zoölogist, François Cetti (1726–80). **C. cetti cetti** (Temminck), Cetti's warbler.

Chætūra Stephens. Coined from Gr. *khaite*, long flowing hair, and *oura*, tail; with ref. to the projecting shafts of the bird's tail-feathers. **C. caudacūta caudacuta** (Latham), needle-tailed swift. "Pointed-tailed"; fem. adj. coined from L. *cauda*, tail, and *acutus*, pointed.

Charadrius Linnæus. Gr. *kharadrios*, a water-bird with inconspicuous plumage and call that keeps out of sight during the day (Aristotle, 614b, 35–36); *kharadra*, torrent, ravine; because it nests in ravines. **C. dubius cūronīcus** Gmelin, little ringed plover. *Dubius*, L., doubtful; because Scopoli, who named the typical form in 1786, was doubtful whether it constituted a distinct species. *Curonicus*, a coined word, meaning "of Courland" (a province of Latvia), where the typical specimen was found; but the bird breeds in widely distributed parts of Europe, Asia and N. Africa. **C. hiāticula hiaticula** Linnæus, ringed plover. *Hiaticula* is Gaza's translation of Aristotle's *kharadrios*, and may mean "the cleft-(bird)," being a fem. dim. from *hiatus*, a cleft, or it may be a mistake for *hiaticola*, cleft-dweller, from *hiatus*, a cleft, and *colo*, inhabit; though the ringed plover does not really frequent clefts. **C. hiāticula semipalmātus** Bonaparte, semi-palmated ringed plover. *Hiaticula*, see above. *Semipalmatus*, semi-palmated; coined from L. prefix *semi-*, half-, and *palmatus*, shaped like the palm of a hand (*palma*); with ref. to the webbing between the bird's toes. **C. hiāticula tundræ** (P. R. Lowe), arctic ringed plover. *Hiaticula*, see under C. *hiaticula hiaticula*. *Tundræ*, latinized gen. of Russian *tundra*; the typical specimen was found on a Siberian tundra, but this is only one of the kinds of habitat where the bird breeds.

Chettūsia Bonaparte. It has been suggested that the name is derived from Gr. *khaitē*, mane, but the form of the name is against this, and the derivation gives no sense; it is more likely that the name is a purely fanciful one, invented by Bonaparte. **C. gregāria** (Pallas), sociable plover. Fem. of L. *gregarius*, belonging to a flock; *grex* (gen. *gregis*), a flock; birds of this kind are nearly always in flocks when not breeding.

Chlamydōtis Lesson. "Mantled-bustard"; coined from Gr. *khlamus* (gen. *khlamudos*), and *otis*, bustard; with ref. to the bird's ruff. **C. undulāta macqueenii** (Gray and Hardwicke), Macqueen's bustard. *Undulata*, fem. of L. *undulatus*, wavy; *unda*, a wave; with ref. to the wavy appearance of the tufts of feathers

---

on the sides of the bird's neck. *Macqueenii*, after Macqueen, who presented the typical specimen to J. E. Gray.

Chlidonias Rafinesque. "Swallow-like"; should be spelt *chelidonias*; from Gr. *khelīdon*, a swallow; with ref. to the tern's swallow-like wings and tail; cf. E. "sea-swallow." There is an old Gr. word *khelidonias*, but that has quite a different meaning. **C. hybrida hybrida** (Pallas), whiskered tern. Fem. of L. *hybridus*, hybrid; the bird was named *Sterna hybrida* by Pallas in 1811, because it seemed to him like a cross between two other species of *Sterna*. As applied to *Chlidonias*, the fem. form, *hybrida*, is a mistake; the masculine form, *hybridus*, should have been used. **C. leucopterus** (Temminck), white-winged black tern. Gr. *leukopteros*, white-winged; *leukos*, white, and *pteron*, a wing; refers to the bird's white shoulders in the breeding-season. **C. niger niger** (Linnæus), black tern. L. *niger*, black; refers to the bird's summer plumage, which is almost entirely blackish.

Chlōris Cuvier. Gr. *khloris*, greenfinch (Aristotle, 592b, 17); from *khloros*, green. **C. chloris chloris** (Linnæus), greenfinch. The prevailing colour of its plumage is olive-green.

Chordeiles Swainson. Apparently a badly coined name from Gr. *khōreo*, to travel, and *deilē*, in the unusual sense of "evening"; the meaning of the name being "evening-traveller"; with ref. to the bird's habit of hunting in the evening. **C. minor minor** (Forster), American nightjar. L. *minor*, lesser. As applied to *Chordeiles* the specific term, *minor*, is meaningless, for there is no other species. Originally, however, the bird was known as *Caprimulgus minor*, and then *minor* was a proper description; for this bird is about 9 in. long, compared with the 10½ in. of *Caprimulgus europæus europæus*, (common) nightjar.

Cicōnia Brisson. L. *ciconia*, stork (Pliny, X, 32). **C. ciconia ciconia** (Linnæus), white stork. **C. nigra** (Linnæus), black stork. Fem. of L. *niger*, black; its upper parts are glossy black.

Cinclus Borkhausen. Gr. *kinklos*, name of a bird mentioned by Aristotle (593b, 6), perhaps a kind of wagtail. **C. cinclus cinclus** (Linnæus), black-bellied dipper. **C. cinclus gulāris** (Latham), British dipper. *Gularis*, adj. coined from L. *gula*, throat; with ref. to the conspicuous whiteness of this part of the bird. **C. cinclus hibernicus** (Hartert), Irish dipper. *Hibernicus*, Irish; coined from L. *Hibernia*, Ireland; breeds not merely in Ireland, but also in the Isle of Man and W. Scotland.

Circus Lacépède. Gr. *kirkos*, a kind of hawk (Aristotle, 620a, 18); perhaps cognate with E. *circle*, with ref. to this bird's circling flight. **C. æruginōsus** *æruginosus* (Linnæus), marsh-harrier. L. *æruginosus*, rusty; *ærugo* (gen. *æruginis*), rust of copper; *æs* (gen. *æris*), copper; with ref. to the bird's colour. **C. cyaneus cyaneus** (Linnæus), hen-harrier. Gr. *kuaneos*, dark blue; with ref. to the male's pearly grey plumage. **C. macrourus** (Gmelin), pallid harrier. "Long-tailed"; coined from Gr. *makros*, long, and *oura*, tail; though this bird's tail is not really noticeably long. **C. pygargus** (Linnæus), Montagu's harrier. Gr. *pugargos*, a kind of eagle (Aristotle, 618b, 19); meaning lit. "white-rumped"; *pūgē*, rump, and *argos*, shining, bright.

Clāmātor Kaup. L. *clamator*, shouter; *clamo*, to call, shout. **C. glandārius** (Linnæus), great spotted cuckoo. *Glandarius* probably here means "jay-like," *glandarius* being the specific name of the jay; in respect of the jay *glandarius* means "eating acorns and beech-mast," from *glans* (gen. *glandis*), acorn, beech-mast; acorns and beech-mast are not the food of the great spotted cuckoo.

Clangula Leach. Coined fem. dim. noun from L. *clango*, to clang; the bird is so called, according to Gesner, on account of the noise that its wings make in flight. **C. hyemālis** (Linnæus), long-tailed duck. L. *hyemalis*, winter-; *hyems*, winter; the bird breeds in or near the arctic region, and comes south only in the winter.

Coccothraustēs Brisson. Gr. *kokko-thraustes*, name of a bird mentioned by

Hesychius; lit. "kernel-breaker," from *kokkos*, kernel, and *thrauo*, shatter; though actually it is fruit stones, not kernels, that the hawfinch breaks. **C. coccothraustes coccothraustes** (Linnæus), hawfinch.

Coccyzus Vieillot. Coined from Gr. *kokkuzo*, to call "cuckoo." **C. americānus americanus** (Linnæus), yellow-billed cuckoo. "American"; a coined word; almost confined to America. **C. erythrophthalmus** (Wilson), black-billed cuckoo. "Red-eyed"; coined from Gr. *eruthros*, red, and *ophthalmos*, eye; with ref. to the red ring round the bird's eyes.

Columba Linnæus, L. *columba*, dove, pigeon; according to Varro, imitative of the bird's call. **C. livia livia** Gmelin, rock-dove. "Blue"; a corruption of *livida*, fem. of L. *lividus*; with ref. to the prevailing colour of the bird's plumage. **C. œnas** Linnæus, stock-dove. Gr. *oinas*, a kind of dove (Aristotle, 544b, 7); perhaps from Gr. *oinos*, wine, with ref. to the bird's colour; but more probably from Hebrew *jonah*, pigeon. **C. palumbus palumbus** Linnæus, wood-pigeon. L. *palumbus*, wood-pigeon.

Colymbus Linnæus. Gr. *kolumbis*, diver (bird), mentioned by Aristotle (487a, 23). **C. adamsii** Gray, white-billed northern diver. After Surgeon C. B. Adams, who discovered the bird in Alaska in 1859. **C. arcticus arcticus** Linnæus, black-throated diver. L. *arcticus*, arctic; breeds mainly in N. Europe. **C. immer** Brünnich, great northern diver. Icelandic *himbrimi*, great northern diver. **C. stellātus** Pontoppidan, red-throated diver. L. *stellatus*, starred; *stella*, a star; with ref. to the white spots on the bird's upper parts in winter.

Coracias Linnæus. Gr. *korakias*, a raven-like bird (Aristotle, 617b, 16); *korax* (gen. *korakos*), raven. **C. garrulus garrulus** Linnæus, roller. L. *garrulus*, talkative; with ref. to its harsh chatter.

Corvus Linnæus. L. *corvus*, raven (Pliny, X, 60); cognate with Gr. *krāzo*, to croak; *corvus* and *krazo* are both imitative of the bird's call. **C. corax corax**

Linnæus, raven. Gr. *korax*, raven (Aristotle, 519a, 5); imitative of the bird's call; cognate with Gr. *krāzo*, to croak. **C. cornix cornix** Linnæus, hooded crow. L. *cornix*, crow (Pliny, VII, 49); imitative of the bird's call; cognate with Gr. *krāzo*, to croak. **C. corōnē corone** Linnæus, carrion-crow. Gr. *korone*, a kind of crow (Aristotle, 609a, 17); imitative of the bird's call; cognate with Gr. *krāzo*, to croak. **C. frūgilegus frugilegus** Linnæus, rook. L. *frugilegus*, crop-picking: *frux* (gen. *frugis*), fruit, crop, and *lego*, pick. A damning and one-sided name—the bird is not altogether a vegetarian. **C. monēdula monedula** Linnæus, Scandinavian jackdaw. L. *monedula*, jackdaw (Pliny, X, 41); derived, according to Albertus Magnus, from *monēta*, money, with ref. to the bird's habit of taking coins; if that view is accepted, we may translate the name as the "money-bird." The bird was indeed a byword among the Ancient Romans for its love of money; Pliny refers to the bird's habit of stealing gold and silver, and according to Ovid (*Metamorphosēs*, VII, 465–8) the bird was originally a nymph, who was transformed into a bird for her greed. **C. monēdula spermologus** Vieillot, jackdaw. *Monedula*, see above. *Spermologus*, Gr. *spermologos*, seed-picker (Aristophanēs: *Birds*, 232); *sperma*, seed, and *lego*, pick; though the bird's food is mainly animal.

Coturnix Bonnaterre. L. *coturnix*, quail (Pliny, X, 33); according to Festus imitative of the bird's call. **C. coturnix coturnix** (Linnæus), quail.

Crex Bechstein. Gr. *krex*, a long-legged bird (Aristotle: *Parts of Animals*, 695a, 21–23), of the size of an ibis (Herodotus, II, 76); imitative of the bird's call. **C. crex** (Linnæus), corn-crake.

Crocēthia Billberg. A coined word; the first part evidently comes from Gr. *krokē*, pebble; the second part may come either from *the(i)o*, to run, or from *ēthos*, accustomed seat, haunt; in either case the reference is to the bird's habit of breeding on stony ground. **C. alba** (Pallas), sanderling. Fem. of L. *albus*, white; with ref. to its winter plumage.

Cucūlus Linnæus. L. *cuculus*, cuckoo (Pliny, XVIII, 66); imitative of the bird's call. **C. canōrus canorus** Linnæus, cuckoo. L. *canorus*, melodious; *cano*, sing.

Cursōrius Latham. L. *cursorius*, meaning originally "of a race-course," but here "addicted to running"; *curso*, run; with ref. to the bird's habit of running instead of flying. **C. cursor cursor** (Latham), cream-coloured courser. L. *cursor*, runner.

Cygnus Bechstein. L. *cygnus*, swan. **C. bewickii bewickii** Yarrell, Bewick's swan. After the British naturalist and artist, Thomas Bewick (1753–1828). **C. cygnus** (Linnæus), whooper swan. **C. olor** (Gmelin), mute swan. L. *olor*, swan (Pliny, X, 32); appears to be of Celtic origin; cf. Welsh *elarch*, Gaelic *eala*, M. Irish *ela*, O. Celtic *elaio*—all meaning "swan."

Delichon Moore. An anagram of *chelīdon*, Gr. for "swallow"; cf. *dacelo*, an anagram of *alcēdo*; *dacelo* is the genus to which the Australian "laughing jackass" belongs, and *alcedo* the genus to which the kingfisher belongs; the evident significance is that the anagrammatic genus is allied to the original genus; frivolous though this method of naming a new genus may seem, it is recognized by the international rules. **D. urbica urbica** (Linnæus), house-martin. Fem. of L. *urbicus*, city-; from *urbs* (gen. *urbis*), city; with ref. to the bird's habit of nesting on houses.

Diomēdea Linnæus. After Diomedes, a Greek warrior who fought at the siege of Troy and whose companions were later transformed into sea-birds. Pliny (X, 61) refers to "the birds of Diomedes ('avēs Diomedeæ')." **D. melanophrys** Temminck, black-browed albatross. Gr. *melanophrus*, black-browed; *melas* (gen. *melanos*), black, and *ophrus*, brow; with ref. to the dark patch round the bird's eye.

Dryobatēs Boic. "Timber-tree frequenting"; coined from Gr. *drus*,

timber-tree, specially oak, and *baino*, go; but there is nothing in the authorities to suggest that the birds of this genus are specially fond of oaks. **D. mājor anglicus** (Hartert), British great spotted woodpecker. *Major*, see below. *Anglicus*, English; coined from L. *Angli*, Angles; confined to the British Isles. **D. mājor major** (Linnæus), northern great spotted woodpecker. L. *major*, greater; about 9½ in. long, compared with the British lesser spotted woodpecker's 5¾ in. **D. minor comminūtus** (Hartert), British lesser spotted woodpecker. *Minor*, L., smaller; about 5¾ in. long, compared with the northern great spotted woodpecker's 9½ in. *Comminutus*, L., diminished; past part. passive of *comminuo*, diminish.

Egretta Forster. Latinized form of Fr. *aigrette*, egret; *aigrette* is the dim. of Provençal *aigron*, heron. **E. alba alba** (Linnæus), great white heron. Fem. of L. *albus*, white; its plumage is pure white. **E. garzetta garzetta** (Linnæus), little egret. Italian *sgarzetta*, little egret; dim. of *sgarza*, great white heron.

Emberīza Linnæus. Latinized form of O. German *embritz* (Gesner); cognate with A.-S. *amore* and E. *hammer* (in *yellow-hammer*). **E. aureola** Pallas, yellow-breasted bunting. Fem. of L. *aureolus*, golden; dim. adj. from *aurum*, gold; with ref. to the bird's yellow breast. **E. brūniceps** Brandt, red-headed bunting. "Brown-headed"; coined from M.L. *brunus*, brown, and classical L. *caput*, head; refers to the male, whose head varies in colour from chestnut to golden. **E. calandra** Linnæus, corn-bunting. Gr. *kalandra*, a kind of lark (Oppian: *Ixeutika*, III, 15); from the resemblance between the two birds. **E. cia cia** Linnæus, rock-bunting. Imitative of the bird's call, "ci ci" (Aldrovandus). **E. cioidēs castaneïceps** Moore, East Siberian meadow-bunting. *Cioides*, like the rock-bunting; coined from *cia*, specific name of rock bunting, and Gr. *eidos*, form, appearance. *Castaneiceps*, L., chestnut-headed; coined from *castanea*, chestnut, and *caput*, head; refers to the colour of the male's crown and nape. **E. cirlus cirlus** Linnæus, cirl bunting. The name used by Aldrovandus; latinized form of *cirlo*, which was the name used in the region of Bologna, N. Italy; probably from Italian *zirlare*, to whistle. **E. citrinella citrinella** Linnæus, yellow bunting. Coined fem. dim. of M.L. *citrinus*, citron-coloured; refers to the male's yellow head and under parts. **E. hortulāna** Linnæus, ortolan bunting. Fem. of L. *hortulanus*, garden-; *hortulus*, dim. of *hortus*, garden; with ref. to one of the numerous kinds of places frequented by this bird. **E. leucocephala** S. G. Gmelin, pine-bunting. Gr. *leukokephalos*, white-headed; *leukos*, white, and *kephalē*, head; with ref. to its white crown. **E. melanocephala** Scopoli, black-headed bunting. "Black-headed"; latinized fem. of an adj. coined from Gr. *melas* (gen. *melanos*), black, and *kephalē*, head; with ref. to the upper part of the male's head in summer. **E. pusilla** Pallas, little bunting. Fem. of L. *pusillus*, petty, small. It is only about 5 in. long, compared with the corn-bunting's 7 in. **E. rustica** Pallas, rustic bunting. Fem. of L. *rusticus*, rustic; what there is particularly rustic about this species is not clear —Pallas found it frequenting willow thickets of Transbaikalia in March. **E. schœniclus compilātor** Mathews and Iredale, western large-billed reed-bunting. *Schœniclus*, see below. *Compilator*, L., robber; *compilo*, (intensive form of *pilo*), rob; but why the bird is so stigmatized is not clear. Perhaps the ref. is to the bird's having originally "robbed" another bird of its name; for this bird was named *Emberiza palustris* in 1829 by Savi, who overlooked the fact that this name had been given to another bird in 1801 by Frenzel. **E. schœniclus schœniclus** (Linnæus), reed-bunting. Gr. *skhoiniklos*, name of a bird mentioned by Aristotle (593b, 6); *skhoinos*, reed; with ref. to the bird's habitat. **E. schœniclus tschusii** Reiser and Almasy, eastern large-billed reed-bunting. *Schœniclus*, see above. *Tschusii*, after the Austrian naturalist, Viktor

Ritter von Tschusi zu Schmidhoffen, whose ornithological bibliography of the Austrian-Hungarian dominions was published in 1878.

Erēmophila Boie. Gr. *eremophilēs*, solitude-loving; *eremos*, lonely, and *phileo*, to love. **E. alpestris flāva** (Gmelin), shore-lark. *Alpestris*, mountain-; coined from *Alpēs*, high mountains; with ref. to the bird's breeding-places. *Flava*, fem. of L. *flavus*, yellow; with ref. to the bird's face and throat.

Erithacus Cuvier. Gr. *erithakos*, a bird which according to Aristotle changes into a redstart in the summer (632b, 28); probably from *eruthros*, red. **E. rubecula melophilus** Hartert, British robin. *Rubecula*, see below. *Melophilus*, song-loving; coined from Gr. *melos*, song, and *phileo*, to love. **E. rubecula rubecula** (Linnæus), continental robin. "Little red one"; Gaza's translation of Gr. *erithakos*; coined fem. dim. from L. *ruber*, red.

Eudromias Brehm. Gr. *eudromias*, good runner; prefix *eu-*, good, and *dromos*, running (noun); the bird's habit is to make a series of short quick runs in search of food. **E. mōrinellus** (Linnæus), dotterel. Coined L. dim. from Gr. *moros*, foolish; similarly *dotterel* is the dim. of *dolt*. The ground of the bird's reputation for stupidity is given by Willughby in what is merely a translation of Gesner. "It is a silly bird," says he, "but as an article of food a great delicacy. It is caught in the night by lamplight, in accordance with the movements of the fowler. For if he stretch out his arm the bird extends a wing; if he a leg, the bird does the same. In short whatever the fowler does the dotterel does the same. And so intent is it on the movements of its pursuer, that it is unawares entangled in the net." Newton, however, thinks that it is the fowler who apes the bird, and not the bird the fowler. A secondary derivation of *morinellus*, according to Gesner, is from *Morini*, the ancient name of the inhabitants of Flanders, where the bird used to abound.

Eupoda Brandt. "Good-footed"; coined from Gr. prefix *eu-*, good, and *pous* (gen. *podos*), foot; like most plovers, a good runner. **E. asiātica asiatica** (Pallas), Caspian plover. Fem. of L. *Asiaticus*, Asiatic; breeds in various parts of Asia and also in S.E. Russia.

Falco Linnæus. M.L. *falco*, falcon; classical L. *falx* (gen. *falcis*), sickle; with ref. to the shape of the bird's talons (Festus). **F. columbārius æsalon** Tunstall, merlin. *Columbarius*, L., originally a noun meaning "pigeon-keeper," but here an adj. meaning "pigeon-"; *columba*, pigeon; with ref. to the bird's occasional capture of a pigeon. *Æsalon*; Gr. *aisalon*, a kind of hawk (Aristotle, 620a, 18). **F. naumanni naumanni** Fleischer, lesser kestrel. After the German ornithologist, Johann Friedrich Naumann (1780–1857). **F. peregrīnus anatum** Bonaparte, North-American peregrine. *Peregrinus*, see below. *Anatum*, gen. plural of L. *anas*, duck; ducks are among the birds on which this peregrine preys. **F. peregrīnus peregrinus** Tunstall, peregrine falcon. L. *peregrinus*, foreign; *per*, through, and *ager* (gen. *agri*), field, territory; the idea conveyed by the derivation being that of a traveller from abroad. Albertus Magnus gives two reasons for the bird's name: (1) that it constantly moves from one place to another; (2) that its nest can never be discovered. **F. rusticolus candicans** Gmelin, Greenland falcon. *Rusticolus*, see under *F. rusticolus rusticolus*. *Candicans*, pres. part. of L. *candico*, be white; the bird's plumage is white with black markings. **F. rusticolus islandus** Brünnich, Iceland falcon. *Rusticolus*, see under *F. rusticolus rusticolus*. *Islandus*, Iceland-; a coined word; almost confined to Iceland. **F. rusticolus rusticolus** Linnæus, gyr-falcon. Mistake for L. *rusticulus*; dim. of *rusticus*, rustic; but why this kind of falcon should have been singled out for this epithet is not clear. **F. subbūteo subbuteo** Linnæus, hobby. "Buzzard-like"; coined from L. prefix *sub-*, akin to, and *buteo*, buzzard (Pliny, X, 9); *subbuteo* is Gaza's trans-

lation of *hupotriorkhēs*, the name mentioned by Aristotle (620a, 20), *sub-* corresponding to *hupo-*, and *buteo* to *triorkhes*; but the significance of the name is not clear. **F. tinnunculus tinnunculus** Linnæus, kestrel. L. *tinnunculus*, kestrel (Pliny, X, 52); the name is a dim. form, and perhaps comes from *tinnio*, to scream; with ref. to the bird's shrill call. **F. vespertinus vespertinus** Linnæus, red-footed falcon. L. *vespertinus*, evening-; *vesper*, evening; the bird hunts moths in the evening.

Frātercula Brisson. Fem. form of M.L. *fraterculus*, friar; dim. of L. *frater*, brother; perhaps with ref. to the bird's habit, when rising from the sea, of clasping its feet as though in prayer. **F. arctica grābæ** (Brehm), southern puffin. *Arctica*, fem. of L. *arcticus*, arctic; not really an arctic bird, its breeding-places extend from the Færoes to Brittany. *Grabæ*, after the German ornithologist, Carl Julian Graba, who discovered the bird on a journey to the Færoes in 1828.

Fringilla Linnæus. L. *fringilla*, finch; a dim. form; according to Festus, from *frigus*, cold (noun), because the bird sings and flourishes in the cold. **F. cœlebs cœlebs** Linnæus, continental chaffinch. L. *cœlebs*, unmarried; from Linnæus's mistaken belief that the females alone migrate; males and females, however, do tend to keep apart in separate flocks during autumn and winter. **F. cœlebs gengleri** Kleinschmidt, British chaffinch. *Cœlebs*, see above. *Gengleri*, after the German ornithologist, J. Gengler. **F. montifringilla** Linnæus, brambling. "Mountain-finch"; coined from L. *mons* (gen. *montis*), mountain, and *fringilla*, finch; breeds chiefly in the mountains of N. Europe and N. Asia.

Fulica Linnæus. L. *fulica*, coot (Pliny, XI, 44); perhaps cognate with L. *fūlīgo*, soot, with ref. to the bird's colour. **F. ātra atra** Linnæus, coot. Fem. of L. *ater*, black; the bird is almost entirely this colour.

Fulmārus Stephens. Latinized form of *fulmar*; see under "Fulmar petrel" in

Galērīda   30   Heteroscelus

List II. F. glaciālis glacialis (Linnæus), fulmar petrel. L. *glacialis*, ice-; *glacies*, ice; with ref. to the bird's habitat.

Galērīda Boie. Mistake for *Galērīta*, L. for crested lark (Pliny, XI, 44); *galea*, helmet, crest. **G. cristāta cristata** (Linnæus), crested lark. Fem. of L. *cristatus*, crested.

Gallīnula Brisson. L. *gallinula*, chicken (Appuleius: *The Golden Ass*, II, 119); dim. of *gallina*, domestic hen; why the name should be given to this genus is not clear. **G. chlōropus chloropus** (Linnæus), moorhen. "Green-footed"; coined from Gr. *khloros*, green, and *pous*, foot.

Garrulus Brisson. L. *garrulus*, talkative. **G. glandārius glandarius** (Linnæus), continental jay. L. *glandarius*, meaning originally "producing acorns or beech-mast," but here "eating acorns and beech-mast"; *glans* (gen. *glandis*), acorn, beech-mast, which form part of the bird's diet in autumn. **G. glandārius hibernicus** Witherby and Hartert, Irish jay. *Glandarius*, see above. *Hibernicus*, Irish; coined from L. *Hibernia*, Ireland; the bird is confined to Ireland. **G. glandārius rūfitergum** Hartert, British jay. *Glandarius*, see under **G.** *glandarius glandarius*. *Rufitergum*, red-backed; coined from L. *rufus* (gen. *rufi*), red, and *tergum*, a back; the neuter form *rufitergum* is an anomaly for the masculine form *rufitergus*.

Gelōchelīdon Brehm. Lit. "laughing-swallow," but here meaning "laughing-tern," the old generic name for tern having been *hydrochelidon*, water-swallow; *gelochelidon* is coined from Gr. *gelos*, laughter, and *khelidon*, swallow; with ref. to the bird's call. **G. nīlōtica nilotica** (Gmelin), gull-billed tern. Fem. of L. *Niloticus*, Nile-; the typical specimen came from the Nile, but the bird also breeds in other parts of N. Africa, in many parts of Europe and in parts of Asia.

Glāreola Brisson. Coined dim. adj. from L. *glarea*, gravel; with ref. to the

bird's supposed habitat, but actually it mostly frequents mud flats. **G. nordmanni** Nordmann, black-winged pratincole. After the Russian naturalist, Alexander von Nordmann (1803–66). **G. prātincola pratincola** (Linnæus), pratincole. "Meadow-dweller"; coined from L. *pratum* (gen. *prati*), meadow, and *incola*, inhabitant; with ref. to one of its kinds of habitat.

Grus Pallas. L. *grus*, crane (Pliny, XI, 44). **G. grus grus** (Linnæus), common crane.

Gyps Savigny. Gr. *gups*, griffon-vulture (Homer: *Iliad* XXII, 42). **G. fulvus fulvus** (Hablizl), griffon-vulture. L. *fulvus*, tawny; with ref. to the prevailing colour of its plumage.

Hæmatopus Linnæus. "Having blood-red feet"; coined from Gr. *haima* (gen. *haimatos*), blood, and *pous*, foot. **H. ostralegus occidentālis** Neumann, British oyster-catcher. *Ostralegus*, oyster-gathering; coined from Gr. *ostreon*, oyster, and *lego*, gather; but the bird does not really gather oysters, though its food consists mainly of shell-fish. *Occidentalis*, L., western; breeds mainly in the British Isles.

Haliaëtus Savigny. Gr. *haliaetos*, sea-eagle (Aristotle, 619a, 4); *hals* (gen. *halos*), sea, and *aetos*, eagle. **H. albicilla** (Linnæus), white-tailed eagle. "White-tailed"; coined from L. *albus*, white, and an imaginary L. word *cilla*, tail. For an explanation of how ornithologists have come to use *cilla* for "tail" see under *Mōtacilla*.

Heteroscelus Baird. Gr. *heteroskelēs*, meaning originally "with uneven legs," but here "with different legs (from other sandpipers)"; *heteros*, different, and *skelos*, leg; the legs of the American race, which gave rise to the generic name, differ from those of all other sandpipers in the scutellation round the tibia and behind the tarsus. **H. incānus brevipes** (Vieillot), grey-rumped sandpiper. *Incanus*, L., grey; with ref. to its upper parts. *Brevipes*, short-footed;

coined from L. *brevis*, short, and *pes*, foot.

Himantopus Brisson. Gr. *himantopous*, a kind of water-bird (Oppian; *Ixeutika*, II, 9); lit. "strap-footed"; *himas* (gen. *himantos*), strap, and *pous*, foot; with ref. to the bird's slender, pliant tarsi. **H. himantopus himantopus** (Linnæus), black-winged stilt.

Hippolaïs Baldenstein. Probably a mistake for *Hypolaïs*, from Gr. *hupolais*, a bird mentioned by Aristotle (618a, 11) as one in whose nest the cuckoo lays its eggs on the ground; perhaps from prefix *hupo-*, like, and *laios* (Aristotle, 617a, 15), a kind of thrush; for this use of *hupo-*, cf. *hupotriorkhes* under *Falco subbuteo subbuteo*. Gesner suggests that the name may be dervied from *hupo*, under, and *lāās*, a stone, with ref. to the bird's habit of searching under stones for insects, but this is unlikely. **H. caligāta caligata** (Lichtenstein), booted warbler. Fem. of L. *caligatus*, booted; *caliga*, boot; with ref. to the continuous covering of the bird's tarsi in place of the usual scales. **H. icterīna** (Vieillot), icterine warbler. "Jaundice-coloured, yellow"; fem. adj. coined from Gr. *ikteros*, which means either jaundice or a yellow bird; according to Pliny (XXX, 28) a sight of the bird would cure anyone suffering from jaundice; this was in accordance with what was known later as the "doctrine of signatures," a principle of which was that natural objects have some outward resemblance to the disease for which they are a cure. **H. pallida elæica** (Lindermayer), olivaceous warbler. *Pallida*, fem. of L. *pallidus*, pale. *Elæica*, latinized fem. of Gr. *elaikos*, like an olive tree; *elaia*, olive tree; with ref. to the pale olive-brown colour of the bird's upper parts. **H. polyglōtta** (Vieillot), melodious warbler. Latinized fem. of Gr. *poluglottos*, many-tongued; *polus*, many, and *glotta*, tongue; with ref. to the bird's vocal powers.

Hirundo Linnæus. L. *hirundo*, a swallow (Pliny X, 49); according to Varro the name is imitative of the bird's call, but it is difficult to understand this. **H.**

daurica rūfula Temminck, red-rumped swallow. *Daurica*, fem. of coined L. *Dauricus*, Daurian; Dauria is another name for Transbaikalia, the region east of Lake Baikal in S.E. Siberia, where the typical species *H. daurica daurica* was found. *Rufula*, fem. of L. *rufulus*, reddish; dim. of *rufus*, red; with ref. to the bird's rump. **H. rustica rustica** Linnæus, swallow. Fem. of L. *rusticus*, country-; as contrasted with the housemartin, which is more addicted to towns and houses than the swallow. **Histriōnicus** Lesson. L. *histrionicus*; adj. from *histrio*, actor; with ref. to the male's gay plumage in summer. **H. histrionicus histrionicus** (Linnæus), harlequin-duck.

Hydrobatēs Boie. "Water-goer;" coined from Gr. *hudōr*, water, and *baino*, go. **H. pelagicus** (Linnæus), storm-petrel. L. *pelagicus*, sea-; *pelagus* (gen. *pelagi*), sea; the bird only comes to land for breeding.

Hydroprognē Kaup. "Water-swallow"; coined from Gr. *hudōr*, water, and *Progne*, an Athenian princess who was turned into a swallow (Ovid; *Metamorphosēs*, VI, 667–70, and Virgil: *Georgics*, IV, 15); with ref. to the tern's swallow-like wings and tail; cf. E. "sea-swallow." **H. caspia** (Pallas), Caspian tern. Fem. of L. *Caspius*, Caspian; the typical specimen came from the Caspian Sea, but the bird breeds in all five continents.

Ixobrychus Billberg. The obvious meaning of this name is "mistletoe-devourer," from Gr. *ixos*, mistletoe, and *brūkho*, devour; but this makes nonsense. Billberg, however, who invented the name in 1828, translates *ixos* by L. *arundo* (reed) and *brukho* by L. *fremo* (to roar, boom), and implies that the meaning of the name is "reed-boomer"; with ref. presumably to the old belief that the (common) bittern produces its "boom" by plunging its bill into a reed and blowing through it. Whether the name can properly bear this meaning is doubtful, for Billberg quotes no authority for his use of *ixos* and seems to have

confused *brukho*, with *brūkhaömai*. **I.
minūtus minutus** (Linnæus), little
bittern. **L.** *minutus*, little; its length is
about 14 in., compared with the (common) bittern's 30 in.

Jynx Linnæus. Gr. *junx*, wryneck
(Aristotle, 504a, 12); perhaps from *iūzo*,
to yell; with ref. to its shrill call. **J.
torquilla torquilla** Linnæus, wryneck.
"Little-twister;" fem. dim. coined from
L. *torqueo*, to twist; with ref. to the
snake-like way in which the bird twists
its neck when captured.

Lagōpus Brisson. Name of a game-bird
mentioned by Pliny (X, 68); lit. "hare-
footed"; Gr. *lagos*, hare, and *pous*, foot;
with ref. to the bird's feathered tarsi and
toes. **L. mūtus millaisi** Hartert,
Scottish ptarmigan. *Mutus*, **L.**, silent;
though it actually croaks, softly. *Millaisi*,
after the British ornithologist, John
Guille Millais (1865–1931). **L. scōticus
hibernicus** (Kleinschmidt), Irish red
grouse. **Scoticus**, see below. *Hibernicus*,
Irish; coined from L. *Hibernia*, Ireland;
resident in Ireland and Outer Hebrides.
L. scōticus scoticus (Latham). "Scottish"; coined from Late L. *Scoti*, a
tribe that lived in S. Scotland and in
Ireland; the bird was originally confined to Great Britain, but was later
introduced into W. Europe.

Lanius Linnæus. L. *lanius*, butcher;
with ref. to its habit of impaling its larger
prey on thorns or other sharp points. **L.
collūrio collurio** Linnæus, red-backed
shrike. Gr. *kollurion*, a bird mentioned
by Aristotle (617b, 10), probably a kind
of thrush. **L. excubitor excubitor**
Linnæus, great grey shrike. L. *excubitor*,
sentinel; lit. "one who lies down out of
doors"; *ex*, out, and *cubo*, lie down;
for once Linnæus explains his meaning—
"Accipitres adventantēs observat et
aviculis indicat" (*Systema Nātūræ*, 10th
ed., I, 94), "it looks out for the approach
of hawks and warns little birds." **L.
excubitor merīdionālis** Temminck,
South European grey shrike. *Excubitor*,
see above. *Meridionalis*, **L.**, southern;

meridies, noon, south; found mainly in
Spain, Portugal and S. France. **L.
minor** Gmelin, lesser grey shrike. L.
minor, smaller; about 8 in. long, compared with the great grey shrike's 9½ in.
L. nūbicus Lichtenstein, masked shrike.
"Nubian"; a coined word; the typical
specimen came from Nubia, which is
one of the places where the bird winters.
L. senātor badius Hartlaub. Corsican
woodchat-shrike. *Senator*, see below.
Badius, **L.**, chestnut-coloured; with ref.
to the bird's crown and nape. **L.
senātor senator** Linnæus, woodchat-
shrike. L. *senator*, senator; what resemblance Linnæus saw between the bird
and a senator it is difficult to say—
perhaps what he had in mind was the
talkativeness of both.

Larus Linnæus. Gr. *laros*, a water-bird
(Aristotle, 593b, 4), probably a gull.
L. argentātus argentatus Pontoppidan,
herring-gull. **L.** *argentatus*, meaning
originally "plated or ornamented with
silver," but here "silver-coloured";
argentum, silver; with ref. to the mature
plumage, which it takes the bird three
years to attain. **L. argentātus omissus**
Pleske, Scandinavian herring-gull.
Argentatus, see above. *Omissus*, **L.**, overlooked; past part. passive of *omitto*;
that is, a form that had escaped attention
before. **L. cānus canus** Linnæus,
common gull. **L.** *canus*, white, hoary;
refers to the prevailing colour of adults.
L. fuscus fuscus Linnæus, Scandinavian
lesser black-backed gull. **L.** *fuscus*, dark;
with ref. to its back. **L. fuscus grællsii**
Brehm, British lesser black-backed gull.
Fuscus, see above. *Grællsii*, after the
Spanish naturalist, Grælls (1818–1898).
L. glaucoidēs Meyer, Iceland gull.
"Like the glaucous gull"; coined from
L. *glaucus*, bluish grey, and Gr. *eidos*, form,
appearance; by "glaucous gull" is
meant *Larus hyperboreus* Gunnerus, which
used to be called *Larus glaucus* Brünnich;
the glaucous gull is bigger, but otherwise very similar to the Iceland one. **L.
hyperboreus** Gunnerus, glaucous gull.
Gr. *huperboreos*, of the extreme north,
arctic; lit. "beyond the North Wind";
huper, beyond, and *Boreas*, (personified)

North Wind; breeds in the arctic region. **L. ichthyaëtus** Pallas, great black-headed gull. "Fish-eagle"; coined from Gr. *ikhthus*, fish, and *aetos*, eagle; with ref. to the bird's main food. **L. marīnus** Linnæus, great black-backed gull. **L.** *marinus*, sea; the bird rarely comes inland. **L. melanocephalus** Temminck. Mediterranean black-headed gull. "Black-headed"; coined from Gr. *melas* (gen. *melanos*), black, and *kephalē*, head; with ref. to the bird's summer plumage. **L. minūtus** Pallas, little gull. **L.** *minutus*, little; it is about 11 in. long, compared with the herring-gull's 22 in. **L. philadelphia** (Ord), Bonaparte's gull. After Philadelphia, U.S.A., where the typical specimen was found; breeds in Canada, but winters as far south as Mexico. An adjectival form, such as *philadelphiensis*, would have been more appropriate. **L. rīdibundus** **ridibundus** Linnæus, black-headed gull. **L.** *ridibundus*, laughing; *rideo*, to laugh; with ref. to its supposedly laughing call.

Leucopolius Bonaparte. "Whitish-grey"; coined from Gr. *leukos*, white, and *polios*, grey; apparently refers to the bird's under parts, but the name is not distinctive. **L. alexandrīnus alexandrinus** (Linnæus), Kentish plover. L. *Alexandrinus*, of Alexandria (Egypt), where the typical specimen was found; but the bird breeds in many places in N. Africa, in Europe and in Asia.

Limicola Koch. **L.** *limicola*, mud-dweller; *limus* (gen. *limi*), mud, and *colo*, inhabit. **L. falcinellus falcinellus** (Pontoppidan), broad-billed sandpiper. "Sickle-"; dim. adj. coined from L. *falx* (gen. *falcis*), sickle; with ref. to the shape of the bird's bill, the tip of which is curved downwards.

Limnodromus Wied. "Marsh-runner"; coined from Gr. *limnē*, marsh, and *dromos*, running (noun); but the bird really walks slowly, though it flies fast. **L. griseus griseus** (Gmelin), red-breasted snipe. M.L. *griseus*, grey; with ref. to its general appearance.

Limōsa Brisson. Fem. of L. *limosus*, meaning originally "muddy," but here

"of the mud"; *limus*, mud; with ref. to the bird's habitat. **L. lappōnica** **lapponica** (Linnæus), bar-tailed godwit. "Of Lapland"; coined fem. adj.; the typical specimen was found in Lapland, but the bird breeds in many parts of N. Europe and N.W. Asia. **L. limosa** **limosa** (Linnæus), black-tailed godwit.

Lōcustella Kaup. "Grasshopper-(bird)"; coined fem. dim. from L. *locusta*, locust; with ref. to the supposed resemblance of the bird's call to a grasshopper's chirrup. **L. certhiola** (Pallas), Pallas's grass-hopper-warbler. Coined dim. of *Certhia*, the generic name of the tree-creeper; which this warbler resembles in respect of the shape of its bill and tail, its colour and its general appearance. **L. lanceo-lāta** (Temminck), lanceolated warbler. Fem. of L. *lanceolatus*, shaped like a little lance; *lanceola*, dim. of *lancea*, lance; with ref. to the pointed streaks on the bird's under parts. **L. luscinioidēs** **luscinioides** (Savi), Savi's warbler. "Nightingale-like"; coined from L. *luscinia*, nightingale (Pliny, X, 43), and Gr. *eidos*, form, appearance. **L. nævia** **nævia** (Boddaert), grasshopper-warbler. Fem. of L. *nævius*, spotted; *nævus*, mole (on the body), spot; with ref. to the markings on the bird's upper parts.

Loxia Linnæus. Coined from Gr. *loxos*, slanting crosswise; with ref. to the arrangement of the bird's mandibles. **L. curvirostra curvirostra** Linnæus, common crossbill. "Bent-billed"; coined fem. adj. from L. *curvus* (gen. *curvi*), curved, bent, and *rostrum*, bill. **L. curvirostra scōtica** Hartert. *Curvi-rostra*, see above. *Scotica*, Scottish; coined fem. adj. from L. *Scoti*, a tribe that lived in S. Scotland and in Ireland; the bird is confined to Scotland. **L. leucoptera bifasciāta** (Brehm), two-barred crossbill. *Leucoptera*, see below. *Bifasciata*, two-banded; coined fem. adj. from L. prefix *bi-*, two, and *fascia*, band, fillet; with ref. to the two white bars on the bird's wings. **L. leucoptera** **leucoptera** Gmelin, American white-winged crossbill. Latinized fem. of Gr. *leukopteros*, white-winged; *leukos*, white,

and *pteron*, feather, wing; with ref. to
the two white bars on the bird's wings.
L. pytyopsittacus Borkhausen, parrot-
crossbill. "Pine-parrot"; should be
spelt *pityopsittacus*; coined from Gr.
pitus, pine, and *psittakos*, parrot; *pitus*,
because pine-forests form the bird's
chief habitat; *psittakos*, with ref. to this
crossbill's parrot-like action—walking
sideways on branches and so on.
Lullula Kaup. A coined word; imitative of the bird's call—"lu-lu-lu." **L.
arborea arborea** (Linnæus), wood-lark.
Fem. of L. *arboreus*, tree-; *arbor*, tree;
not a very suitable name—the bird does
indeed perch on trees, but it feeds on the
ground.
Luscinia Forster. L. *luscinia*, nightingale
(Pliny X, 43); according to Varro from
luctus, lamentation, and *cano*, sing,
because its song was thought to be
mournful; but this derivation, in spite
of its antiquity, seems unlikely. **L.
luscinia** Linnæus, thrush-nightingale. **L.
megarhyncha megarhyncha** Brehm,
nightingale. "Great-billed"; L. fem.
adj. coined from Gr. *megas*, great, and
rhunkhos, bill; but the greatness of the
bird's bill is not obvious. **L. svēcica
cyanecula** (Meisner), white-spotted bluethroat. *Svecica*, see below. *Cyanecula*,
coined L. fem. dim. from Gr. *kuanos*,
blue; with ref. to the marking on the
bird's throat. **L. svēcica svecica**
(Linnæus), red-spotted bluethroat.
"Swedish"; coined fem. adj. from L.
Sueones, a tribe that inhabited S.
Sweden; the typical specimen was
found in Sweden, but the bird breeds in
many parts of N. Europe and N.W.
Siberia.
Lusciniola Gray. L. *lusciniola*, little
nightingale (Varro; *Dē Rē Rusticā*, III,
5, 14); dim. of *luscinia*, which see. **L.
melanopōgōn melanopogon** (Temminck), moustached warbler. "Black-
bearded"; coined from Gr. *melas* (gen.
melanos), black, and *pogon*, beard; with
ref. to the black patch on the bird's lores
and below its eyes.
Lymnocryptēs Boie. "Marsh-hider";
should be spelt *Limnocryptes*; coined
from Gr. *limnē*, marsh, and *krupto*, hide;

with ref. to the bird's habit of hiding
among reeds before it is flushed. **L.
minimus** (Brünnich), jack snipe. L.
minimus, smallest; its length is about
7½ in., compared with the common
snipe's 10½ in.
Lyrūrus Swainson. "Lyre-tailed";
coined from Gr. *lura*, lyre, and *oura*,
tail; because the bird's tail is shaped like
a lyre. **L. tetrix britannicus** Witherby
and Lönnberg, British black grouse.
Tetrix, Gr., an unknown bird mentioned
by Aristotle (559a, 3); but here apparently confused with Gr. *tetraōn*, which
was used in its L. form *tetrao* by Pliny
(X, 29) to mean a kind of grouse.
Britannicus, L., British; confined to
Great Britain.

Melanitta Boie. "Black duck"; coined
from Gr. *melas* (gen. *melanos*), black, and
nētta, duck. **M. fusca fusca** (Linnæus),
velvet-scoter. Fem. of L. *fuscus*, dark.
M. nigra nigra (Linnæus), common
scoter. Fem. of L. *niger*, black; refers
particularly to the male, which is almost
entirely glossy black—the female is
dark brown. **M. perspicillāta**
(Linnæus), surf-scoter. Coined fem.
intensive form of L. *specillatus*, which
meant originally "furnished with
mirrors"; *speculum*, mirror; here,
however, *speculum* has the modern
ornithological meaning of a patch of
feathers whose colour is in marked
contrast to that of the surrounding
ones; the ref. is to the two white
patches on the male bird's head and
nape.

Melanocorypha Boie. Gr. *melankoruphos*,
name of a bird mentioned by Aristotle
(592b, 22), perhaps the blackcap; lit.
"black-crowned", from *melas* (gen.
melanos), black, and *koruphē*, crown (of
the head). But the name does not
appear suitable for this genus; for the
male of the typical species, the black
lark, is black all over and not merely
on its crown, while the other two
British species have not black crowns
at all. It looks indeed as if Boie intended

the name to mean "black lark," but that is a meaning that it cannot properly bear. **M. calandra calandra** (Linnæus), calandra lark. Gr. *kalandra*, a kind of lark (Oppian; *Ixeutika*, III, 15). **M. leucoptera** (Pallas), white-winged lark. Latinized fem. of Gr. *leukopteros*, white-winged; *leukos*, white, and *pteron*, wing; with ref. to the bird's having a white bar on its wings and being white under its wing coverts. **M. yeltoniensis** (Forster), black lark. "Of Lake Yelton (or Elton)"; the typical specimen was found in this region, near the lower Volga in S. Russia.

Mergus Linnæus. L. *mergus*, diver (bird), mentioned by Pliny (XVIII, 87); *mergo*, plunge (transitive). **M. albellus** Linnæus, smew. "Whitish"; dim. coined from L. *albus*, white; refers particularly to the male, whose plumage is mainly white. **M. cucullātus** Linnæus, hooded merganser. M.L. *cucullatus*, originally meaning "monk," but here "hooded"; M.L. *cuculla* (classical L. *cucullus*), cowl; refers particularly to the male's conspicuous cowl-like crest of white and black—the female also has a crest, but it is buff and smaller. **M. merganser** Linnæus, goosander. "Diver-goose"; coined from L. *mergus*, diver, and *anser*, goose; *anser* may refer to the size of the bird, which is the largest of all kinds of duck, the male being about 26 in. long, compared with the mallard's 23 in. **M. serrātor** Linnæus, red-breasted merganser. M.L. *serrator*, sawyer; classical L. *serra*, a saw; with ref. to the saw-like teeth on the edges of the bird's mandibles.

Merops Linnæus. Gr. *merops*, bee-eater (Aristotle 626a, 9); derivation unknown. A word of identical spelling is used in the plural (*meropes*) by Homer as an epithet of men, with the meaning of "articulate"; in this sense *merops* is probably derived from *merīzo*, divide, and *ops*, voice (Hesychius); but the bird's name seems to have quite a different origin. **M. apiaster** Linnæus, bee-eater. Masculine form coined from fem. L. *apiastra*, bee-eater (Servius: commentary on Virgil; *Georgics*, IV,

14); *apis*, bee; the bird feeds mainly on bees and wasps.

Milvus Lacépède. L. *milvus*, kite (Pliny X, 12). **M. migrans migrans** (Boddaert), black kite. Pres. part. of L. *migro*, migrate; with ref. to its migration to tropical Africa in winter. **M. milvus** *milvus* (Linnæus), kite.

Monticola Boie. L. *monticola*, mountain-dweller; *mons* (gen. *montis*), mountain, and *colo*, inhabit. **M. saxātilis** (Linnæus), rock-thrush. L. *saxatilis*, rock-dweller; *saxum*, rock.

Montifringilla Brehm. "Mountain-finch"; coined from L. *mons* (gen. *montis*), mountain, and *fringilla*, finch. **M. nivālis nivalis** (Linnæus), snow-finch. L. *nivalis*, snow-; *nix* (gen. *nivis*), snow; with ref. to the bird's habitat on high mountains.

Mōtacilla Linnæus. L. *motacilla*, wagtail (Varro); apparently from an assumed word *motax* (gen. *mōtācis*), continually moving (transitive); *motax* itself would be derived from *moto*, intensive form of *moveo*, move (on the analogy of *tenax*, tenacious, from *teneo*, hold); *-illa* is a fem. dim. termination; the literal meaning, therefore, is "little mover." A curious misapprehension, however, has grown up among ornithologists, who have imagined that *cilla* is L. for "tail" and have even invented new names on that supposition, e.g. *albicilla*, white-tailed (eagle), the name of a species of *Haliaëtus*, and *Bombȳcilla*, wax-wing, a name that refers to the bird's yellow-tipped tail. The misapprehension dates back at least to the fourteenth century, for Gaza translated *phoinīkouros*, Aristotle's name for a redstart, by *ruticilla*; *phoinikouros* is derived from *phoinix* (gen. *phoinikos*), crimson, and *oura*, tail; the first part of *ruticilla* comes from *rutilus*, red; so *cilla* was obviously taken by Gaza to mean "tail." The origin of the misapprehension is to be found in a failure to understand Varro's explanation of the name *motacilla*. He said that the bird owes its name to the fact that it is always moving its tail (*caudam*, accusative of *cauda*); and this clearly gave rise to the idea that as *mota*, the first part of the name, meant "moving," *cilla*, the second part of the name, meant "tail." It is obvious, however, that if there had been such a word as *cilla*, Varro would have said in his explanation of *motacilla* that the bird moves its *cilla*, not its *cauda*. **M. alba alba** Linnæus, white wagtail. Fem. of *L. albus*, white; with ref. to the bird's forehead, sides of its head and its under parts. **M. alba persōnāta** Gould, masked wagtail. *Alba*, see above. *Personata*, fem. of *L. personatus*, masked; *persona*, a mask; with ref. to the mask-like white patch in front of its crown and round and behind its eyes. **M. alba yarrellii** Gould, pied wagtail. *Alba*, see under *M. alba alba*. *Yarrellii*, after the British naturalist, William Yarrell (1784–1856). **M. cinerea cinerea** Tunstall, grey wagtail. Fem. of *L. cinereus*, ash-coloured; *cinis* (gen. *cineris*), ashes; with ref. to the bird's blue-grey upper parts. **M. flāva beema** (Sykes), Sykes's wagtail. *Flava*, see under *M. flava flava*. *Beema* (the adj. form *beemensis* would have been more regular), from the river Bhima, in Hyderabad and Bombay, where the typical specimen was found; the bird does not breed in India, but winters there and in E. Africa. **M. flāva cinereocapilla** Savi, ashy-headed wagtail. *Flava*, see under *M. flava flava*. *Cinereocapilla*, "with ash-coloured hairs on head"; fem. adj. coined from L. *cinis* (gen. *cineris*), ashes, and *capillus*, hair of the head. **M. flāva feldegg** Michahelles, black-headed wagtail. *Flava*, see under *M. flava flava*. Feldegg, the gen. form *Feldeggi* would have been more regular; after Ritter Freiherr von Feldegg of Spalatro (Split, Dalmatia), who provided the typical specimen. **M. flāva flava** Linnæus, blue-headed wagtail. Fem. of L. *flavus*, yellow; with ref. to its under parts. **M. flāva flavissima** (Blyth), yellow wagtail. *Flava*, see above. *Flavissima*, most yellow; fem. of *flavissimus*, superlative of L. *flavus*, yellow; not only are the bird's under parts yellow, but in summer the male's head is yellow also. **M. flāva thunbergi** Billberg, grey-headed wag-

tail. *Flava*, see under *M. flava flava*. *Thunbergi*, after the Swedish naturalist and traveller, C. P. Thunberg (1743–1828).

Muscicapa Brisson. "Flycatcher"; coined from L. *musca*, fly, and *capio*, seize. **M. albicollis** Temminck, collared flycatcher. "White-necked"; coined from L. *albus* (gen. *albi*), white, and *collum*, neck; refers to the male's plumage. **M. hypoleuca hypoleuca** (Pallas), Pied flycatcher. Latinized fem. of Gr. *hupoleukos*; which originally meant "whitish," from prefix *hupo-*, somewhat, and *leukos*, white; but which here apparently means "white underneath," *hupo* being used in the prepositional sense of "under," with ref. to the male's plumage in summer. **M. lātirostris** Raffles, brown flycatcher. "Broad-billed"; coined from L. *latus* (gen. *lati*), broad, and *rostrum*, bill; with ref. to the very broad base of the bird's bill. **M. parva parva** Bechstein, red-breasted flycatcher. Fem. of L. *parvus*, small; the bird is about 4½ in. long, compared with the spotted flycatcher's 5½ in. **M. striāta striata** (Pallas), spotted flycatcher. "Striped"; coined fem. adj. from L. *stria*, a furrow; with ref, to the markings on the bird's head and breast.

Neophrōn Savigny. After Neophron, a youth who according to Greek mythology was turned into a vulture by the god Zeus (Antōnīnus Līberālis; *Transformations*, VII). **N. percnopterus percnopterus** (Linnæus), Egyptian vulture. Gr. *perknopteros*, a kind of eagle (Aristotle 618b, 32); lit. "dark-winged"; *perknos*, dark, and *pteron*, wing; the primaries of the bird's wings are black.

Nētta Kaup. Gr. *netta*, duck (Aristotle 593b, 19). **N. rūfīna** (Pallas), red-crested pochard. Fem. adj. coined from L. *rufus*, red; with ref. to the male's head and bill.

Nucifraga Brisson. "Nut-breaker"; coined from L. *nux* (gen. *nucis*), nut, and *frango*, break; with ref. to its habit of breaking open nuts for food. **N. caryocatactēs caryocatactes** (Linnæus), thick-billed nutcracker. Gr. *karuokataktes*, nutcracker (Hesychius); *karuon*, nut, and *katasso*, shatter. **N. caryocatactes macrorhynchus** Brehm, slender-billed nutcracker. *Caryocatactes*, see above. *Macrorhynchus*, Gr. *makrorrhunkhos*, long-billed; *makros*, long, and *rhunkhos*, bill; that is, with a bill longer than the thick-billed nutcracker's. **Nūmēnius** Brisson. Gr. *noumenios*, a kind of curlew (Diogenēs Laërtius, IX, 114); lit. "the new-moon (bird)"; Gr. *neos*, new, and *mēnē*, moon; with ref. to the bird's crescent-shaped bill. **N. arquāta arquata** (Linnæus), common curlew. M.L. *arquata*, curlew; classical L. *arquatus*, bent; *arquatus* itself is derived from *arcus*, a bow (weapon); with ref. to the shape of the bird's bill (Gesner). **N. boreālis** (Forster), Eskimo curlew. L. *borealis*, northern; Gr. *Boreas*, (personified) North Wind; used to breed in N. Mackenzie, Canada, but now almost extinct. **N. phæopus phæopus** (Linnæus), whimbrel. "Grey-footed"; coined from Gr. *phaios*, grey, and *pous*, foot; the bird's legs are greenish grey, but so are the common curlew's. **N. tenuirostris** Vieillot, slender-billed curlew. "Slender-billed"; coined from L. *tenuis*, slender, and *rostrum*, bill; the slenderness of the bird's bill is not obvious.

Nyctea Stephens. Gr. *nuktios*, night-; *nux* (gen. *nuktos*), night; but this bird usually comes out by day. **N. scandiāca** (Linnæus), snowy owl. "Scandinavian"; L. *Scandia*, ancient name of the southern extremity of Sweden; breeds in the arctic region of Europe, Asia and America.

Nycticorax Forster. Gr. *nuktikorax*, a long-eared owl (Aristotle, 597b, 22–24); lit. "night-raven"; *nux* (gen. *nuktos*), night, and *korax*, raven; the bird usually comes out only at night. **N. nycticorax nycticorax** (Linnæus), night-heron.

Ōceänītēs Keyserling and Blasius. Gr. *Okeanitis*, daughter of (personified) Ocean; *Okeanos*, Ocean; keeps to the open sea except during the breeding-season. **O. ōceänicus** (Kuhl), Wilson's petrel. "Ocean-"; coined from L. *oceanus*, ocean.

Ōceänodroma Reichenbach. "Ocean-running"; coined from Gr. *Okeanos*, (personified) Ocean, and *dromos*, running (noun); spends its time on the open sea except during the breeding-season. **O. castro** (Harcourt), Madeiran fork-tailed petrel. From *Roque* (rook) *de Castro*, the bird's name in the Deserta Islands, Madeira (Harcourt; *Sketch of Madeira*, 1851, p. 123). **O. leucorrhoä leucorrhoa** (Vieillot), Leach's fork-tailed petrel. "White-rumped"; latinized fem. adj., coined from Gr. *leukos*, white, and *orrhos*, rump.

Œnanthē Vieillot. Gr. *oinanthe*, name of a bird mentioned by Aristotle (633a, 15), perhaps the wheatear; lit. "vine-blossom (bird)"; *oinē*, vine, and *anthē*, blossom; perhaps because the bird appears in Greece at the same time as the vine-blossom—according to Aristotle the bird arrives at the setting of the dog-star. **O. dēserti ātrogulāris** (Blyth), eastern desert-wheatear. *Deserti*, see below. *Atrogularis*, should be spelt *atrigularis*; lit. "black-throated"; coined from L. *ater* (gen. *atri*), black, and *gula*, throat; with ref. to the male. **O. dēserti deserti** (Temminck), desert-wheatear. "Desert-"; gen. of L. *desertum*, a desert; found in deserts of N. Africa and central Asia. **O. dēserti homochroä** (Tristram). *Deserti*, see above. *Homochroä*, latinized fem. of Gr. *homokhroös*, of one colour; *homos*, same, and *khrōs*, skin, colour. The name is based on a curious mistake. The male is far from being "of one colour"; for it has a conspicuous black throat. The typical bird, however, that Tristram, the author of the name, happened to examine was a female; which is, loosely speaking, "of one colour" when compared with the males of (common) desert-wheatears, as its throat is of the same colour as the surrounding parts. **O. hispānica hispanica** (Linnæus), western black-eared wheatear. Fem. of L. *Hispanicus*, Spanish; breeds in the

Mediterranean region. **O. hispānica melanoleuca** (Güldenstädt), eastern black-eared wheatear. *Hispanica*, see above. *Melanoleuca*, "black-white"; latinized fem. adj., coined from Gr. *melas* (gen. *melanos*), black, and *leukos*, white; with ref. to the male's summer plumage, which is often almost pure black and white. **O. isabellïna** (Temminck), isabelline wheatear. Coined L. fem. adj., meaning "greyish-yellow," "sand-coloured." As regards the derivation of the word, Isaac D'Israeli, father of Lord Beaconsfield, gives the following account (*Curiosities of Literature*, article on "Anecdotes of Fashion"): "Fashions have frequently originated from circumstances as silly as the following one. Isabella, daughter of Philip II and wife of the Archduke Albert, vowed not to change her linen till Ostend was taken; this siege, unluckily for her comfort lasted three years; and the supposed colour of the archduchess's linen gave rise to a fashionable colour, hence called *l'Isabeau*, or the Isabella; a kind of whitish-yellow-dingy." A delicious story, but alas! shown by the Oxford English Dictionary to be untrue—as far, at any rate, as relates to the colour and the origin of its name. For there is proof that the name existed before the siege of Ostend even began. The siege began in July, 1601; and in July, 1600, the following entry appeared in the inventory of the wardrobe of Queen Elizabeth (of England): "Item, one rounde gowne of Isabella-colour. . . ." The real origin of the name is now unknown. **O. leucomela leucomela** (Pallas), pied wheatear. Barbarous quasi-Latin fem. of Gr. *leukomelas*, originally meaning "whitish black," but here apparently "white and black"; *leukos*, white, and *melas*, black. **O. leucūra leucura** (Gmelin), black wheatear. Latinized fem. of Gr. *leukouros*, white-tailed; *leukos*, white, and *oura*, tail. **O. leucūra syēnïtica** (Heuglin), North African black wheatear. *Leucura*, see above. *Syenitica*, of Assouan, Egypt; coined fem. adj. from L. *Syēnē*, ancient name of Assouan; the specimen bird was found in upper Egypt, but the bird

usually breeds in a more northerly part of Africa. **O. œnanthē leucorrhoä** (Gmelin), Greenland wheatear. **Leucorrhoa**, white-rumped; coined from Gr. *leukos*, white, and *orrhos*, rump. **O. œnanthē œnanthe** (Linnæus), wheatear. **Oriolus** Linnæus. M.L. *oriolus*, golden; classical L. *aureolus*, from *aurum*, gold; with ref. to the colour of the male's plumage except for its black wings and tail. **O. oriolus oriolus** (Linnæus), golden oriole.

Ōtis Linnæus. Gr. *otis*, a kind of bustard (Aristotle 619b, 13); *ous* (gen. *otos*), ear; with ref. to its long ear-feathers. **O. tarda tarda** Linnæus, great bustard. *Tarda*, latinized form of an ancient Spanish name for a kind of bustard (Pliny X, 29); the name, therefore, has nothing to do with L. *tardus*, slow, in spite of the attempts of some ornithologists to connect the name with the bird's stately walk. **O. tetrax orientālis** Hartert. *Tetrax*, see below. *Orientalis*, L., eastern; breeds in E. Europe and S.W. Asia. **O. tetrax tetrax** Linnæus, western little bustard. *Tetrax*, the Gr. name for two kinds of birds, the larger of which is apparently here referred to; according to Athēnæus (398c) it was a brightly-coloured table-bird, larger than any domestic cock, with wattles hanging from its ears and with a low-pitched voice—perhaps a pheasant. *Tetrax* is cognate with Urdu *tītar*, partridge.

Ōtus Pennant. Gr. *otos*, a kind of owl with long ear-feathers (Aristotle, 597b, 18); *ous* (gen. *otos*), ear. **O. scōps scops** (Linnæus), scops-owl. Gr. *skops*, probably the little horned owl (Aristotle, 592b, 11). The name is said to come from *skopeo*, look at; with ref. to the bird's habit of staring (Athēnæus, 629f).

Oxyēchus Reichenbach. Gr. *oxuekhos*, sharp-sounding; *oxus*, sharp, and *ekheo*, to sound. **O. vōciferus vociferus** (Linnæus), killdeer plover. "Screaming"; coined from L. *vociferor*, to scream.

Pagophila Kaup. "Frost-lover"; coined from Gr. *pagos*, frost. and *phileo*, to love; the bird's main habitat is the arctic icepack. **P. eburnea** (Phipps), ivory-gull.

Fem. of L. *eburneus*, ivory-coloured; *ebur*, ivory; the adult's plumage is pure white.

Pandīon Savigny. After Pandion, king of Attica, but Savigny seems to have confused the legend. Pandion's two daughters were changed into birds and so was Tereus, who married one of them, but not Pandion himself. **P. haliaëtus haliaetus** (Linnæus), osprey. Gr. *haliaetos*, sea-eagle (Aristotle, 619a, 4); *hals* (gen *halos*), sea, and *aetos*, eagle; only found near water, but not necessarily the sea.

Panūrus Koch. "All-tail"; coined from Gr. *pas* (gen. *pantos*), all, and *oura*, tail; with ref. to the bird's long tail. **P. biarmicus biarmicus** (Linnæus), bearded tit. Perhaps a corruption of *beardmanica* ("bearded manikin"), the barbarous name invented by Albin and referred to by Linnæus (*Systēma Nātūræ*; 10th edition, I, 190); with ref. to the male's black moustache.

Pārus Linnæus. L. *parus*, tit (*Carmen dē Philomēlā*). **P. āter ater** Linnæus, continental coal-tit. L. *ater*, black; with ref. to its black crown. **P. āter britannicus** Sharpe and Dresser, British coal-tit. *Ater*, see above. *Britannicus*, L., British; confined to Great Britain. **P. āter hibernicus** Ogilvie-Grant, Irish coal-tit. *Ater*, see under *P. ater ater*. *Hibernicus*, Irish; coined from L. *Hibernia*, Ireland; confined to Ireland. **P. ātricapillus boreālis** Selys-Longchamps, northern willow-tit. *Atricapillus*, L., black-crowned; *ater* (gen. *atri*), black, and *capillus*, hair of the head. *Borealis*, L., northern; Gr. *Boreas*, (personified) North Wind; confined to N. Europe. **P. ātricapillus kleinschmidti** Hellmayr, British willow-tit. *Atricapillus*, see above. *Kleinschmidti*, after the German ornithologist, Otto Kleinschmidt. **P. cæruleus cæruleus** Linnæus, continental blue tit. L. *cæruleus*, sky-blue; *cælum*, sky; with ref. to the bird's crown. **P. cæruleus obscūrus** Prazak, British blue tit. *Cæruleus*, see above. *Obscurus*, L., dark; the British bird is rather darker than the continental one. **P. cristātus cristatus** Linnæus, northern crested tit. L. *cristatus*,

crested; *crista*, crest. **P. cristātus mitrātus** Brehm, Central European crested tit. *Cristatus*, see above. *Mitratus*, mitred; derived ultimately from Gr. *mitra*, turban, but coined directly from M.L. *mitra*, mitre; with ref. to the shape of the bird's crest. **P. cristātus scōticus** (Prazak), Scottish crested tit. *Cristatus*, see under *P. cristatus cristatus*. *Scoticus*, Scottish; coined from late L. *Scoti*, a tribe that lived in S. Scotland and in Ireland; the bird is confined to Scotland. **P. mājor major** Linnæus, continental great tit. L. *major*, greater; it is about 5½ in. long, compared with the continental blue tit's 4½ in. **P. mājor newtoni** Prazak, British great tit. *Major*, see above. *Newtoni*, after the British ornithologist, Alfred Newton (1829–1907). **P. palustris dresseri** Stejneger, British marsh-tit. L. *palustris*, marsh-; *palus*, marsh; though the bird does not really specially frequent marshes. *Dresseri*, after the British ornithologist, Henry Eeles Dresser (1838–1915).

Passer Brisson. L. *passer*, sparrow (Pliny, X, 52). **P. domesticus domesticus** (Linnæus), house-sparrow. L. *domesticus*, house-; *domus*, house; found specially near houses and on cultivated land. **P. montānus montanus** (Linnæus), tree-sparrow. L. *montanus*, mountain-; *mons* (gen. *montis*), mountain; but the bird does not really frequent mountains.

Pastor Temminck. L. *pastor*, shepherd; with ref. to the bird's habit of perching on sheep's backs in search of ticks. **P. roseus** (Linnæus), rose-coloured starling. L. *roseus*, rose-coloured; with ref. to the bird's back and under parts.

Pelagodroma Reichenbach. Gr. *pelagodromos*, sea-running; *pelagos*, sea, and *dromos*, running (noun); the bird stays at sea except when breeding. **P. marīna hypoleuca** (Webb, Berthelot and Moquin-Tandon), frigate-petrel. *Marina*, fem. of L. *marinus*, sea-; the bird only comes to land for breeding. *Hypoleuca*, latinized fem. of Gr. *hupoleukos*; the original meaning is "whitish," from prefix *hupo-*, somewhat, and *leukos*, white, but here the meaning seems to be "white underneath," *hupo*

4—(C.174)

being used in the prepositional sense of "under"; with ref. to the bird's white under parts.

Perdix Brisson. L. *perdix*, partridge (Pliny, X, 51); after Perdix, the nephew of the mythical Athenian sculptor, Dædalus; Perdix was changed into a bird, which was said to have been named after him (Ovid: *Metamorphoses*, VIII, 236–59); but the youth may have been called after the bird instead of the bird after the youth. **P. perdix perdix** (Linnæus), common partridge.

Pernis Cuvier. Corruption of Gr. *pternis*, a kind of hawk (Aristotle, 620a, 19). **P. apivorus apivorus** (Linnæus), honey-buzzard. "Bee-eater"; coined from L. *apis*, bee, and *voro*, devour; the bird eats wild bees and honey, but its chief food is wasp grubs.

Phalacrocorax Brisson. L. *phalacrocorax*, cormorant (Pliny, X, 68 and XI, 47), lit. "bald crow"; Gr. *phalakros*, bald, and *korax*, crow; the cormorant is not really bald, but perhaps the ref. is to the southern cormorant, whose head and neck have rather a bald-like appearance from their hoary feathers. **P. aristotelis aristotelis** (Linnæus), shag. After Aristotle; presumably with ref. to the water-bird whose name he gives as *korax* (593b, 20); but the bird meant by Aristotle seems to be the cormorant and not the shag; for he says that it nests on trees, a thing that the shag is never known to do but which the cormorant does occasionally. **P. carbo carbo** (Linnæus), cormorant. L. *carbo*, charcoal; with ref. to the colour of the bird's plumage, which is bronze-brown and black. **P. carbo sinensis** (Shaw and Nodder), southern cormorant. *Carbo*, see above. *Sinensis*, Chinese; coined from *Sinæ*, a tribe that lived in S.W. China; the typical specimen was found in China, but the bird breeds in many other parts of Asia and in many parts of Europe.

Phalaropus Brisson. "Coot-footed"; should be *phalaridopus*; coined from Gr. *phalaris* (gen. *phalaridos*), coot, and *pous*, foot; with ref. to the lateral lobes on the bird's toes. **P. fulicarius** (Linnæus),

grey phalarope. "Coot-like"; coined from L. *fulica*, coot; with the same significance as the generic name. **P. lobatus** (Linnæus), red-necked phalarope. "Lobed"; coined from Late L. *lobus*, Gr. *lobos*, lobe; with ref. to the bird's toes.

Phasianus Linnæus. Gr. *phasianos*, pheasant (Aristotle, 559a, 25); from *Phasis*, a river in ancient Colchis (on the east coast of the Black Sea), where the bird was found (Pliny, X, 67). **P. colchicus**, pheasant. L. *Colchicus*, of Colchis; see above.

Philomachus Anonymous. Gr. *philomakhos*, warlike; Gr. *phileo*, to love, and *makhē*, fighting; with ref. to the male's aggressive display at the breeding-season. **P. pugnax** (Linnæus), ruff. L. *pugnax*, warlike; *pugno*, to fight; for the same reason as the generic name.

Phœnicopterus Linnæus. Gr. *phoinikopteros*, flamingo (Aristophanes: *Birds*, 273); lit. "crimson-winged"; *phoinix* (gen. *phoinikos*), crimson (called after the Phœnicians, who first discovered and used this colour), and *pteron*, wing. **P. ruber roseus** Pallas, flamingo. *Ruber*, L., red. *Roseus*, L., rose-coloured.

Phœnicurus Forster. Gr. *phoinikouros*, redstart (Aristotle, 632b, 29); lit. "crimson-tailed"; *phoinix* (gen. *phoinikos*), crimson (called after the Phœnicians, who first discovered and used this colour), and *oura*, tail. **P. ochrurus gibraltariensis** (Gmelin), black redstart. *Ochrurus*, "pale-tailed"; coined from Gr. *okhros*, pale, and *oura*, tail; but the name seems inappropriate. *Gibraltariensis*; a coined word; the typical specimen was found at Gibraltar, but the bird breeds in many other parts of Europe and also in Morocco. **P. phœnicurus phœnicurus** (Linnæus), redstart.

Phylloscopus Boie. "Leaf-explorer"; coined from Gr. *phullon*, leaf, and *skopeo*, look at; with ref. to the bird's habit of exploring leaves for insects. **P. borealis borealis** (Blasius), Eversmann's warbler. L. *borealis*, northern; Gr. *Boreas*, (personified) North Wind; breeds in N. Europe and N. Asia. **P. collybita**

abietīnus (Nilsson), Scandinavian chiff-chaff. *Collybita*, see below. *Abietinus*, M.L., meaning originally "made of fir," but here "fir-haunting"; L. *abies* (gen. *abietis*), fir. **P. collybita collybita** (Vieillot), chiffchaff. Probably a mistake for *collybistēs*, from Gr. *kollubistes*, money-changer; the equivalent of the Normandy name of the bird, *compteur d'argent*; its monotonous call being taken to resemble the sound of a money-changer counting out his money. **P. collybita tristis** Blyth, Siberian chiffchaff. *Collybita*, see above. *Tristis*, L., sad; with ref. to the bird's plaintive call. **P. fuscātus fusca-tus** (Blyth), dusky warbler. L. *fuscatus*, dark; past part. passive of *fusco*, darken; darker than other warblers, without any green or yellow in its plumage. **P. inornātus inornatus** (Blyth), yellow-browed warbler. L. *inornatus*, unadorned, plain; prefix *in-*, not, and *ornatus*, past part. passive of *orno*, adorn. As applied to a warbler, *inornatus* is pointless, but Blyth's name for the bird was *Rēgulus inornatus*, not *Phylloscopus inornatus*; and the specific term referred to the absence of the conspicuous crest that characterizes the other species of the genus *Regulus* (goldcrests). **P. prōrēgulus proregulus** (Pallas), Pallas's warbler. "Goldcrest-masquerader"; coined from L. prefix *pro-*, instead of, and generic name *Regulus*, goldcrest; with ref. to the resemblance between the two birds. **P. schwarzi** (Radde), Radde's bush-warbler. After the Russian astronomer, Schwartz, who led an expedition to Siberia in 1852. **P. sībilātrix** (Bech-stein), wood-warbler. L. *sibilatrix*, whistling; *sibilo*, to whistle; with ref. to the bird's trilling song. **P. trochiloi-dēs viridānus** Blyth, greenish warbler. *Trochiloides*, like the willow-warbler; coined from *trochilus*, specific name of the willow-warbler, and Gr. *eidos*, form, appearance. *Viridanus*, greenish; coined from L. *viridis*, green. **P. trochilus ācrēdula** (Linnæus), northern willow-warbler. *Trochilus*, see below. *Acredula*, L., an unknown bird (Cicero: *On Divination*, I, 8); why the name has been assigned to this warbler is not clear. **P. trochilus trochilus** Linnæus),

willow-warbler. Aristotle uses *trokhilos* as the name of two distinct birds: (i) the plover that picks the crocodile's teeth (612a, 20–24), and (ii) the gold-crest (615a, 17–20). Linnæus must have had the second meaning in mind when he applied the name of *trochilus* to the willow-warbler; but even so it is inappropriate. *Trokhilos* is derived from *trekho*, to run; perhaps with ref. to the goldcrest's constant flitting.

Pīca Brisson. L. *pica*, magpie (Pliny, X, 59); perhaps imitative of one of its calls. **P. pica pica** (Linnæus), magpie.

Pīcus Linnæus. L. *picus*, woodpecker (Pliny, X, 20); perhaps imitative of one of its calls. According to a legend Picus was the son of Saturn and was changed into a woodpecker (Ovid: *Metamorphosēs*, XIV, 388–96); but the divinity may have been called after the bird instead of the bird after the divinity. **P. viridis pluvius** Hartert, green wood-pecker. *Viridis*, L., green. *Pluvius*, L., rain-; *pluo*, to rain; with ref. to the belief that this bird's call is a presage of rain.

Pīnicola Vieillot. "Pine-dweller"; coined from L. *pinus* (gen. *pini*), pine, and *colo*, inhabit; the bird particularly frequents pine forests. **P. ēnucleātor enucleator** (Linnæus), pine-grosbeak. "Kernel-remover"; coined from L. *enucleo*, take out the kernel; derived from prefix *e-*, out, and *nucleus*, kernel, which itself comes from *nux* (gen. *nucis*), nut; with ref. to the bird's habit of extracting kernels from berries.

Platalea Linnæus. L. *platalea*, spoonbill (Cicero: *On the Nature of the Gods*, II, 49); Gr. *platus*, broad, with ref. to the broad front of the bird's bill. **P. leucorodia leucorodia** Linnæus, spoon-bill. "White-red"; coined from Gr. *leukos*, white, and *rhodeos*, rosy; the bird's plumage is entirely white except for a reddish tinge on the adult's breast.

Plēctrophenax Stejneger. The original name was *Plēctrophanēs*, "spur-dis-playing," and was coined from Gr. *plektron*, a spur, and *phaino*, to display;

with ref. to the bird's long hind-claw.
For technical reasons Stejneger changed
this name to *Plectrophenax*; his object
was to make as little change as possible,
but *phenax*, Gr. for "impostor," seems
pointless. **P. nivālis nivalis** (Linnæus),
snow-bunting. L. *nivalis*, snow-; *nix*
(gen. *nivis*), snow; with ref. to the bird's
habitat when breeding.

Plēgadis Kaup. "Sickle-(bird)"; coined
from Gr. *plegas*, sickle; with ref. to the
shape of the bird's bill, which is curved
downwards. **P. falcinellus falcinellus**
(Linnæus), glossy ibis. "Sickle-like";
dim. adj., coined from L. *falx* (gen.
falcis), sickle; for the same reason as
Plegadis.

Pluviālis Brisson. L. *pluvialis*, rain-;
pluvia, rain. Many explanations of the
name have been given: Belon says the
bird is so called because plovers are
caught most easily in rainy weather
(but this is not true); Charleton,
because they haunt rain-soaked places;
Littré, because they arrive in flocks in
the rainy season; another authority
(quoted by Newton), because some
kinds of plover have markings on their
upper plumage like rain-drops; another
(mentioned in the Oxford English
Dictionary), because the birds foretell
rain by their restlessness; while the
German name *Regenpfeifer* (rain-piper)
implies that the bird sings in the rain.
Perhaps the real origin of the name is
that plovers like rain in a general sort of
way. **P. aprīcāria altifrons** (Brehm),
northern golden plover. *Apricaria*, see
below. *Altifrons*, high-browed; coined
from L. *altus* (gen. *alti*), high, and *frons*,
brow; but this is not a marked
characteristic. **P. aprīcāria apricaria**
(Linnæus), southern golden plover. Fem.
adj., coined from L. *apricus*, which
meant originally "exposed to the sun,"
but apparently here means "sun-tinged";
with ref. to the bird's "golden" colour.
P. dominica dominica (P. L. S.
Müller), American golden plover. "Of
San Domingo (West Indies)"; a coined
fem. adj.; with ref. to the place where
the typical specimen was found; the
bird breeds in N. Canada, but winters in

S. America. **P. dominica fulva**
(Gmelin), Asiatic golden plover.
Dominica, see above, but this bird breeds
in N. Siberia and winters in more
southerly parts of Asia and in Australia,
New Zealand and Oceania. *Fulva*, fem.
of L. *fulvus*, tawny.

Pōdiceps Latham. A contraction of the
original name *podicipes*, "vent-footed";
coined from L. *podex* (gen. *podicis*), vent,
and *pes*, foot; with ref. to the position
of the bird's legs, which are inserted far
behind the middle of its body. **P.
aurītus** (Linnæus), Slavonian grebe. L.
auritus, long-eared; *auris*, ear; with ref.
to the tufts of feathers that project behind
the eyes in the summer plumage. **P.
cristātus cristatus** (Linnæus), great
crested grebe. L. *cristatus*, crested;
crista, crest. **P. griseīgena griseigena**
(Boddaert), red-necked grebe. "Grey-
cheeked"; coined from M.L. *griseus*,
grey, and classical L. *gena*, cheek;
griseigena has the termination of a fem.
adj., but *Podiceps* is masculine. **P.
griseīgena holboellii** Reinhardt,
American red-necked grebe. *Griseigena*,
see above. *Holboellii*, after the Danish
ornithologist, Holböll (1795–1856), who
discovered the bird in Greenland. **P.
nigricollis nigricollis** Brehm, black-
necked grebe. "Black-necked"; coined
from L. *niger* (gen *nigri*), black, and
collum, neck. **P. rūficollis ruficollis**
(Pallas), little grebe. "Red-necked";
coined from L. *rufus* (gen. *rufi*), red, and
collum, neck.

Polysticta Eyton. Latinized fem. of Gr.
polustiktos, many-spotted; *polus*, many,
and *stizo*, to prick. **P. stelleri** (Pallas),
Steller's eider. After the German
naturalist and traveller, Georg Wilhelm
Steller (1709–1746), who discovered the
bird in Kamchatka.

Porzāna Vieillot. According to Gesner
sporzana was the name used round
Ferrara, N. Italy. **P. carolīna** (Linnæus),
Carolina crake. After Carolina, U.S.A.,
where some specimen birds were
obtained, but birds of this species breed
in many parts of N. America and winter
as far south as Peru. An adjectival form,
such as *carolinensis*, would be more

appropriate as the specific term than the noun form *carolina*. **P. parva** (Scopoli), little crake. Fem. of L. *parvus*, small; its length is about 7½ in., compared with the spotted crake's 9 in. **P. porzana** (Linnæus), spotted crake. **P. pusilla intermedia** (Hermann), Baillon's crake. *Pusilla*, fem. of L. *pusillus*, diminutive; its length is about 7½ in., compared with the spotted crake's 9 in. *Intermedia*, fem. of L. *intermedius*, intermediate; that is, between the water-rail and the spotted crake, the former of which resembles Baillon's crake in colour, and the latter in the size and shape of its bill; all three birds belonged in Hermann's time to the genus *Rallus*, their scientific names being, respectively, Baillon's crake, *Rallus intermedius*; water-rail, *Rallus aquāticus*; spotted crake, *Rallus porzana*.

Prūnella Vieillot. According to Gesner fowlers called the bird by this name on account of its "dark red" colour. The name appears, therefore, to be a fem. dim. of M.L. *prunus* (or *brunus*), brown. **P. collāris collaris** (Scopoli), alpine accentor. "Neckbanded"; coined from L. *collare* (pronounced *collarey*), neckband; with ref. to the appearance of the bird's speckled throat. **P. modulāris hebridium** Meinertzhagen, Hebridean hedge-sparrow. *Modularis*, see below. *Hebridium*, of the Hebrides; latinized gen. **P. modulāris modularis** (Linnæus), continental hedge-sparrow. "Warbling"; coined from L. *modulor*, to warble. **P. modulāris occidentālis** (Hartert), British hedge-sparrow. *Modularis*, see above. *Occidentalis*, L., western; confined to British Isles and W. France.

Pterodroma Bonaparte. "Wing-runner"; coined from Gr. *pteron*, wing, and *dromos*, running (noun); perhaps with ref. to the bird's wild flight. **P. hasitāta** (Kuhl), capped petrel. The meaning of *hasitata* is a problem. It first appears in Forster's unpublished plates as the name of a species of *Procellāria*, and was adopted by Kuhl in 1820. In 1863, however, Schlegel (in his account of *Procellaria neglecta*) refers to Kuhl's *Procellaria hæsitata*, which

suggests that *hasitata* is a mistake for *hæsitata*. If so, *hæsitata* appears to be the fem. of an adj. coined from L. *hæsito*, hesitate, and having the meaning of "uncertain"; the idea being that it was uncertain whether the bird belongs to a distinct species. **P. leucoptera brevipes** (Peale), collared petrel. *Leucoptera*, latinized fem. of Gr. *leukopteros*, white-winged; *leukos*, white, and *pteron*, wing; with ref. to the under-coverts of the bird's wings. *Brevipes*, short-footed; coined from L. *brevis*, short, and *pes*, foot. **P. neglecta** (Schlegel), kermadec petrel. Fem. of L. *neglectus*, ignored; past part. passive of *negligo*, ignore; because the species had not received attention before.

Puffīnus Brisson. Latinized form of E. *puffin*, which see in List II; the use of this word for a shearwater seems to have arisen from confusion on the part of Ray. **P. assimilis barōli** (Bonaparte), Madeiran little shearwater. *Assimilis*, L., similar; as applied to this bird the name is absurd, as it means that the bird is "like" itself; for the typical form, the Australian bird *Puffinus assimilis assimilis*, was so called on account of its resemblance to this very Madeiran little shearwater, which then bore the name of *Puffinus obscurus*. *Baroli*, after the Marchese Farlotti di Barol of Turin. **P. assimilis boydi** Mathews, Cape Verde little shearwater. *Assimilis*, L., similar; the typical form, the Australian bird *Puffinus assimilis assimilis*, was so called on account of its resemblance to the Madeiran little shearwater. *Boydi*, after the British ornithologist, Boyd Alexander, who discovered the bird in the Rombo Islands, Cape Verde group, in 1897. **P. gravis** (O'Reilly), great shearwater. L. *gravis*, heavy; its length is 17–18 in., compared with the little shearwater's 11 in. **P. griseus** (Gmelin), sooty shearwater. M.L. *griseus*, grey; not an appropriate name—the bird's upper parts are sooty black-brown and its under parts grey-brown. **P. kuhlii boreālis** Cory, North Atlantic shearwater. *Kuhlii*, see below. *Borealis*, L., northern; Gr. *Boreas*, (personified) North Wind; breeds on islands in eastern N.

Atlantic. **P. kuhlii kuhlii** (Boie), Mediterranean shearwater. After the German naturalist, Heinrich Kuhl (1797–1821). **P. l'herminiëri l'herminieri** Lesson, Audubon's shearwater. After L'Herminier, a creole ornithologist of Guadeloupe, West Indies. **P. puffinus maurētānicus** Lowe, Balearic shearwater. *Mauretanicus*, adj. coined from L. *Mauretania*, the ancient name for the country that roughly included modern Morocco, Algeria and Libya; the typical specimen came from Algeria. **P. puffinus puffinus** (Brünnich), Manx shearwater.

Pyrrhocorax Tunstall. Gr. *purrhokorax*, chough (Pliny, X, 68); lit. "flame-coloured raven"; *purrhos*, flame-coloured, and *korax*, raven; *purrhos* itself comes from *pur*, a fire; with ref. to the bird's bright red bill and legs. **P. pyrrhocorax pyrrhocorax** (Linnæus), chough.

Pyrrhūla Brisson. Latinized form of Gr. *purrhoulas*, bullfinch (Aristotle 592b, 22); *purrhos*, flame-coloured; *purrhos* itself comes from *pur*, a fire; with ref. to the male's bright red under parts. **P. pyrrhula nēsa** Mathews and Iredale, British bullfinch. *Nesa*, perhaps a mistake for *nesæa*, latinized fem. form of Gr. *nesaios*, island-; with ref. to the bird's being British and not continental. **P. pyrrhula pyrrhula** (Linnæus), northern bullfinch.

Rallus Linnæus. Latinized form of German *ralle*, rail (bird); imitative of the bird's call, cf. E. "rattle." **R. aquāticus aquaticus** Linnæus, water-rail. L. *aquaticus*, water-.

Recurvirostra Linnæus. "With bill bent back"; coined from L. *recurvus* (gen. *recurvi*), bent back, and *rostrum*, bill; the front of the bill is curved upwards. **R. avosetta** Linnæus, avocet. Italian *avocetta*, avocet; perhaps derived from L. *avis*, bird; the dim. termination *-etta* might here imply gracefulness.

Rēgulus Cuvier. L. *regulus*, little king; dim. of *rex* (gen. *regis*), king; with ref. to the goldcrest's being dubbed "king

of the birds" (Aristotle, 615a, 17–20). How the name arose is unknown, but possibly the crest suggested a crown. The earliest record that we have of the use of *regulus* as the name of a bird belongs to about A.D. 500 (*Carmen dē Philomēlā* 13); Albertus Magnus also refers to the nickname (under *crochilus*, a corruption of *trokhilos*, the Gr. name for the goldcrest). The idea persisted in later bird-lore, except that the bird was taken to be a wren. **R. ignicapillus ignicapillus** (Temminck), firecrest. "Fire-haired"; coined from L. *ignis*, fire, and *capillus*, hair of the head; with ref. to the bird's fire-like crest. **R. regulus anglōrum** Hartert, British goldcrest. *Anglorum*, L., of the English; gen. of *Angli*, Englishmen; the bird is confined to the British Isles. **R. regulus regulus** (Linnæus), continental goldcrest.

Rhodostēthia MacGillivray. "Rose-breasted"; coined from Gr. *rhodon*, rose, and *stethos*, breast. **R. rosea** (MacGillivray), Ross's gull. Fem. of L. *roseus*, rosy; with ref. to the colour of the bird's breast.

Ripāria Forster. Fem. of L. *riparius* (Pliny, XXX, 12), nesting in banks; *ripa*, bank. **R. riparia riparia** (Linnæus), sand-martin.

Rissa Stephens. Icelandic *rita*, kittiwake. **R. tridactyla tridactyla** (Linnæus), kittiwake. Latinized fem. of Gr. *tridaktulos*, three-toed; prefix *tri-*, three, and *daktulos*, finger, toe; only the three front toes of the bird are of appreciable size, the hind one being very diminutive.

Saxicola Bechstein. "Stone-dweller"; coined from L. *saxum* (gen. *saxi*), stone, and *colo*, inhabit; with ref. to the habitat of some species. **S. rubetra** (Linnæus), whinchat. Gaza's translation of Aristotle's *batis* (592b, 17); coined fem. adj. from L. *rubus*, bramble-bush; with the suggestion that the bird frequents brambles, though it actually prefers gorse (cf. its common name). **S. torquāta hībernans** (Hartert), British stonechat. *Torquata*, fem. of L. *torquatus*, adorned with a collar; *torques*, collar; with ref. to the white patch on the sides of the male's neck. *Hibernans*, L., wintering; pres. part. of *hiberno*; with ref. to the fact that some birds stay in the British Isles for the winter. **S. torquāta maura** (Pallas), Siberian stonechat. *Torquata*, see under *S. torquata hibernans*. *Maura*, fem. of L. *Maurus*, Moroccan; with ref. to the bird's winter-quarters—the common name refers to its breeding-place. **S. torquāta theresæ** Meinertzhagen, Hebridean stonechat. *Torquata*, see under *S. torquata hibernans*. *Theresæ*, after the British entomologist, Miss Theresa Clay, who is the niece of Col. R. Meinertzhagen, the author of the name, and who accompanied and assisted him on many of his expeditions.

Scolopax Linnæus. Gr. *skolopax*, woodcock (Aristotle 614a, 33); *skolops* (gen. *skolopos*), anything pointed, a stake; perhaps with ref. to the bird's bill. **S. rusticola** Linnæus, woodcock. A mistake for *rusticula*; name of a bird that runs on the ground (Pliny, X, 54); lit. "the little country-(bird)"; fem. dim. of *rusticus*, country-; with ref. to the bird's haunting woods instead of marshes or water like other members of the family, such as snipes and sandpipers.

Serīnus Koch. Latinized form of Fr. *serin*; see under "Serin" in List II. **S. canārius serinus** (Linnæus), serin. *Canarius*, coined from *Canaria*, the classical L. name of one of the Canary Islands; the bird having been first brought from these islands to the mainland of Europe. *Canaria* means lit. "(The Isle) of Dogs", being derived from *canis*, dog, and was so called on account of the giant breed of dogs that abounded there (Pliny, VI, 37)—the dogs are still there, looking rather like Great Danes or mastiffs.

Sitta Linnæus. Gr. *sittē*, a bird that lives by pecking the bark of trees (Aristotle, 616b, 22), probably the nuthatch. **S. europæa affīnis** Blyth, British nuthatch. *Europæa*, fem. of L. *Europæus*, European; confined to Great Britain. *Affinis*, L., related to; with ref. to the bird's close

resemblance to the central European bird (*Sitta europæa cæsia*).

Sōmateria Leach. "Body-wool (bird)," "down (bird)"; coined from Gr. *soma* (gen. *somatos*), body, and *erion*, wool; with ref. to the bird's famous down. **S. mollissima mollissima** (Linnæus), common eider. Fem. superlative of L. *mollis*, soft; with ref. to its down. **S. spectābilis** (Linnæus), king-eider. L. *spectabilis*, showy; lit. "fit to be seen"; *specto*, see; with ref. to the conspicuous orange knob at the base of the male's bill in the breeding-season.

Spatula Boie. L. *spat(h)ula*, dim. of *spatha*, a broad, flat instrument for stirring liquids; with ref. to the bird's broad-fronted bill. **S. clypeāta** (Linnæus), shoveler. Fem. past part. passive of *clypeo*, furnish with a shield; with ref. to the broad shield-like front of the bird's bill.

Squātarōla Cuvier. The Venetian name. **S. squatarola** (Linnæus), grey plover.

Stercorārius Brisson. L. *stercorarius*, derived from *stercus*, dung, but apparently here meaning "offal-(bird)"; with ref. to what the birds of this genus feed on at times. **S. longicaudus** Vieillot, long-tailed skua. "Long-tailed"; coined from L. *longus* (gen. *longi*), long, and *cauda*, tail; with ref. to the extremely long middle feathers of the bird's tail. **S. parasīticus** (Linnæus), arctic skua. L. *parasiticus*, parasitic; because it robs other birds of their prey. **S. pōmarīnus** (Temminck), pomatorhine skua. Mistake for *pomatorhinus*, lid-nosed; coined from Gr. *poma* (gen. *pomatos*), lid, and *rhis* (gen. *rhinos*), nose; with ref. to the rim over the base of the bird's bill in summer. **S. skua skua** (Brünnich), great skua. Icelandic *skufr*, skua; perhaps imitative of the bird's call.

Sterna Linnæus. The O.E. name, mentioned by William Turner in 1544 in his book on the birds of Pliny and Aristotle (under *Gavia*); cognate with Danish *terne*, Swedish *tärna*. **S. albifrons albifrons** Pallas, little tern. "With a white forehead"; coined from L. *albus* (gen. *albi*), white, and *frons*, forehead;

with ref. to the bird's summer plumage.
S. anæthētus anæthetus Scopoli,
bridled tern. Mistake for *anæsthetus*;
Gr. *anaisthetos*, unfeeling, stupid;
apparently because it lets men approach
so near; that is the reason why Linnæus
called a similar bird *Sterna solida*, "the
stupid tern" (*Systēma Nātūræ*, 10th ed.,
I, 137), and why English sailors have
called it "noddy." As applied to *Sterna*,
the fem. form *anætheta* should have been
used, not the masculine form *anæthetus*.
S. dougallii dougallii Montagu, roseate
tern. After Dr. MacDougall of Glasgow,
who provided the typical specimen in
1812. **S. fuscāta fuscata** Linnæus,
sooty tern. Fem. of L. *fuscatus*, dark;
past part. passive of *fusco*, darken; with
ref. to the bird's upper parts. **S. hirundo
hirundo** Linnæus, common tern. L.
hirundo, a swallow; with ref. to the
bird's swallow-like wings and tail; cf.
the popular name "sea-swallow." **S.
macrūra** Naumann, arctic tern. "Long-
tailed"; latinized fem. adj., coined from
Gr. *makros*, long, and *oura*, tail. **S.
sandvicensis sandvicensis** Latham,
sandwich tern. "Sandwich-"; a coined
word; after the place where the typical
specimen was found in 1784.

Streptopelīa Bonaparte, "Collar-dove";
coined from Gr. *streptos*, (i) twisted, (ii)
collar, and *peleia*, a kind of dove (Homer:
Odyssey, XV, 527); with ref. to the
black and white patch on the sides of
the bird's neck. **S. orientālis orientalis**
(Latham), eastern rufous turtle-dove.
L. *orientalis*, eastern; breeds in E. Asia.
S. turtur turtur (Linnæus), turtle-dove.
L. *turtur*, turtle-dove (Pliny, X, 52);
imitative of the bird's call.

Strix Linnæus. L. *strix*, screech-owl;
Gr. *strīzo*, to screech. **S. aluco sylvātica**
Shaw, British tawny owl. *Aluco*, used
by Gaza as a translation of Aristotle's
name *eleos* (592b, 12); latinized form of
the O. Italian name *alocho* (Gesner).
Sylvatica, fem. of L. *sylvaticus*, wood-;
sylva, wood; with ref. to the bird's
chief habitat.

Sturnus Linnæus. L. *sturnus*, starling
(Pliny, X, 35). **S. vulgāris vulgaris**
Linnæus, starling. L. *vulgaris*, common.

S. vulgāris zetlandicus Hartert, Shetland starling. *Vulgaris*, see above.
Zetlandicus, Shetland-; a coined word;
the bird is confined to the Shetland
Islands and Outer Hebrides.

Sula Brisson. Norwegian *sula*, gannet.
S. bassāna (Linnæus), gannet. "Of the
Bass Rock" (at the entrance of the
Firth of Forth); a coined fem. adj.;
with ref. to a well-known breeding-
place of the bird, but there are also about
a dozen other breeding-places in the
British Isles and other places in the N.
Atlantic.

Surnia Duméril. Apparently an arbi-
trary name. **S. ulula caparoch** (Müller).
American hawk-owl. *Ulula*, see below.
Caparoch, from *coparacoch*, the name used
by American Indians round Hudson's
Bay, which is the bird's typical locality.
S. ulula ulula (Linnæus), European
hawk-owl. L. *ulula*, screech-owl (Pliny,
X, 16); imitative of the bird's call.

Sylvia Scopoli. "The woodland-(bird)"
coined from L. *sylva*, wood. **S. ātricapilla atricapilla** (Linnæus), blackcap.
Fem. of L. *atricapillus*, black-haired;
ater (gen. *atri*), black, and *capillus*, hair
of the head; with ref. to the male's black
cap. **S. borin** (Boddaert), garden-
warbler. The old Genoese name
(Aldrovandus); from L. *bos*, ox; because
the bird originally so called was reputed
to keep close to oxen. **S. cantillans
cantillans** (Pallas), subalpine warbler.
Pres. part. of L. *cantillo*, warble; dim.
of *canto*, sing. **S. commūnis communis**
Latham, whitethroat. L. *communis*,
common. **S. currūca blythi** Ticehurst
and Whistler, Siberian lesser whitethroat.
Curruca, see below. *Blythi*, after the
British ornithologist, Edward Blyth
(1810–1873). **S. currūca curruca**
(Linnæus), lesser whitethroat. L. *curruca*,
some kind of bird (Juvenal, VI, 276);
Gesner suggests that the name is imitative of the bird's call, but it is difficult to
understand this. **S. hortensis hortensis**
(Gmelin), orphean warbler. L. *hortensis*,
garden-; *hortus*, garden; with ref. to
one of the habitats of this bird. **S.
melanocephala melanocephala** (Gmelin), Sardinian warbler. "Black-headed";

coined from Gr. *melas* (gen. *melanos*), black, and *kephalē*, head. **S. nīsōria** (Bechstein), barred warbler. "Like a sparrow-hawk"; fem. adj. coined from M.L. *nisus*, sparrow-hawk; with ref. to the bird's under parts. **S. rüppelli** Temminck, Rüppell's warbler. After the German traveller and ornithologist, W. P. E. S. Rüppell (1794–1884), who discovered the bird in Crete. **S. undāta dartfordiensis** Latham, Dartford warbler. *Undata*, undulating; coined fem. adj. from L. *unda*, wave; with ref. to the bird's flight. *Dartfordiensis*, Dartford-; a coined word; the typical specimen was found near Dartford, Kent, in 1773; breeds mainly in Hampshire and Surrey.

Syrrhaptēs Illiger. Lit. "the sewn-together (bird)"; Gr. *surrhapto*, sew together; prefix *sur-*, together, and *rhapto*, sew; with ref. to the junction of the bird's three front toes—it has no hind one. **S. paradoxus** (Pallas), Pallas's sand-grouse. Gr. *paradoxos*, originally meaning "contrary to opinion," but here "abnormal"; *para*, beyond, and *doxa*, opinion; with ref. to the unique arrangement of the bird's foot and other abnormal features.

Tadorna Boie. Latinized form of Fr. *tadorne*, sheld-duck. **T. tadorna** (Linnæus), sheld-duck.

Tetraö Linnæus. L. *tetrao*, a kind of grouse (Pliny, X. 29); from Gr. *tetraōn*, pheasant; cognate with Urdu *tītar*, partridge. **T. ūrogallus urogallus** Linnæus, capercaillie. "Mountain-cock"; coined by Gesner from the German *auerhahn*; *uro-* is the latinized form of *auer-*, mountain-, and *gallus* is the L. translation of *hahn*, cock.

Tīchodroma Illiger. "Wall-runner"; coined from Gr. *teikhos*, wall, and *dromos*, running (noun); with ref. to the bird's habit of climbing walls (and rocks). **T. mūrāria** (Linnæus), wall-creeper. "Wall-"; coined fem. adj. from L. *murus*, wall.

Tringa Linnæus. Gr. *trungas*, a white-rumped water-bird (Aristotle, 593b, 5).

T. erythropus (Pallas), spotted red-shank. Gr. *eruthropous*, a red-footed bird (Aristophanēs; *Birds*, 303); *eruthros*, red, and *pous*, foot. **T. flāvipes** (Gmelin), yellowshank. "Yellowfoot"; coined from L. *flavus* (gen. *flavi*), yellow, and *pes*, foot. **T. glāreola** Linnæus, woodsandpiper. "The little gravel-(bird)"; coined fem. dim. from L. *glarea*, gravel; though the bird's main habitat is really marshes. **T. melanoleuca** (Gmelin), greater yellowshank. "Black-and-white"; latinized fem. adj., coined from Gr. *melas* (gen. *melanos*), black, and *leukos*, white; with ref. to the bird's upper parts, though they are really dark-brown and white. **T. nebulāria** (Gunnerus), greenshank. Fem. adj. coined from L. *nebula*, mist; the idea comes from the Norwegian vernacular name *skodde-fole*, lit. "mist-foal"; with ref. to the bird's habitat, which consists mostly of marshes. **T. ōchropus** Linnæus, green sandpiper. "Pale-footed"; coined from Gr. *okhros*, pale, and *pous*, foot; but the name does not seem appropriate for this bird, its feet being greenish. **T. sōlitāria solitaria** Wilson, solitary sandpiper. Fem. of L. *solitarius*, solitary; birds of this species are usually found singly or in pairs. **T. stagnātilis** (Bechstein), marsh-sandpiper. L. *stagnatilis*, marsh-; *stagnum*, marsh; with ref. to the bird's habitat. **T. totanus britannica** Mathews, British red-shank. *Totanus*, see under *T. totanus totanus*. *Britannica*, fem. of L. *Britannicus*, British; breeds in the British Isles. **T. totanus rōbusta** (Schiöler), Iceland red-shank. *Totanus*, see under *T. totanus totanus*. *Robusta*, fem. of L. *robustus*, solid, hardy; with ref. to the bird's large size. **T. totanus totanus** (Linnæus), continental redshank. Latinized form of Italian *totano*, redshank.

Trōglodytēs Vieillot. Gr. *troglodutes*, hole-frequenter; *trōglē*, hole, and *duo*, enter; with ref. to the bird's habit of continually seeking cover. **T. trōglodytēs hebridensis** Meinertzhagen, Hebridean wren. "Hebridean"; a coined word; the bird is confined to the Outer Hebrides. **T. trōglodytēs hirtensis**

Seebohm, St. Kilda wren. Adj. coined from Gaelic *Hirta*, St. Kilda (lit. "The Western Land"); the bird is confined to St. Kilda. **T. trōglodytēs troglodytes** (Linnæus), wren. **T. trōglodytēs zetlandicus** Hartert, Shetland wren. "Shetland-"; a coined word; the bird is confined to the Shetland Islands. **Tryngītēs** Cabanis. "Tringa-like"; a coined word; the first part of the word comes from Gr. *trungas*, the origin of *Tringa*, the name of a genus (which see); the suffix *-ites* seems to be a mistake for *-oides*, from Gr. *eidos*, appearance, form. **T. subrūficollis** (Vieillot), buff-breasted sandpiper. "Reddish-necked"; a coined word; the first part of the word comes from L. *subrufus* (gen. *subrufi*), reddish, which itself comes from prefix *sub-*, somewhat, and *rufus*, red; the second part of the word comes from L. *collum*, neck; an inappropriate name—not only the bird's neck, but the whole of its under parts, including its throat, and the sides of its face are buff. **Turdus** Linnæus. L. *turdus*, thrush (Pliny, X, 36). **T. dauma aureus** Holandre, White's thrush. *Dauma*, from the Bengali name *dāma*, the typical form of the species being a resident of N. India. *Aureus*, L., golden; *aurum*, gold; with ref. to the bird's yellowish upper parts. **T. erīcētōrum ericetorum** Turton, British song-thrush. "Of the heaths"; gen. plural of M.L. *ericetum*, heath; Gr. *ereikē*, heather; a fallacious name—the bird mainly frequents gardens, woods and hedges; for the origin of the mistake see p. 8. **T. erīcētōrum hebridensis** Clarke, Hebridean song-thrush. *Ericetorum*, see above, but this bird really does frequent heaths. *Hebridensis*, Hebridean; a coined word; the bird is confined to the Hebrides. **T. erīcētōrum philomelus** Brehm, continental song-thrush. *Ericetorum*, see under *T. ericetorum ericetorum*. *Philomelus*, song-lover; coined from Gr. *phileo*, to love, and *melos*, song; perhaps intended to suggest Philomēla, who according to Greek legend was the daughter of Pandīōn, king of Athens, and was changed into a nightingale;

with ref. to this song-thrush's fine song. **T. eunomus** Temminck, dusky thrush. Gr. *eunomos*, well-ordered; prefix *eu-*, well, and *nomos*, law; perhaps with ref. to the large communities in which this bird lives in the winter. **T. merula merula** Linnæus, blackbird. L. *merula*, blackbird (Pliny, X, 42); according to Varro, (fem.) dim. of *merus*, alone (though its usual meaning is "pure," "unmixed"); because each bird is inclined to keep to itself, that is, outside the breeding season. **T. mūsicus coburni** Sharpe, Iceland redwing. *Musicus*, see below. *Coburni*, after the British ornithologist, F. Coburn, who procured three type specimens in N. Iceland in 1899. **T. mūsicus musicus** Linnæus, redwing. L. *musicus*, musical; but the name seems to have no special application to this bird. **T. pilāris** Linnæus, fieldfare. Used by Gaza as the L. translation of *trikhas*, the name used by Aristotle for a kind of thrush (617a, 20); Gaza apparently coined *pilaris* from L. *pilus*, hair, on the assumption that *trikhas* is derived from *thrix* (gen. *trikhos*), hair, but he was probably mistaken. **T. rūficollis ātrogulāris** Jarocki, black-throated thrush. *Ruficollis*, red-necked; coined from L. *rufus* (gen. *rufi*), red, and *collum*, neck; this bird has not anything red about its neck, but it ranks as a form of the non-British *T. ruficollis ruficollis*, which has a red throat. *Atrogularis*, black-throated; mistake for *atrigularis*; coined from L. *ater* (gen. *atri*), black, and *gula*, throat; with ref. to the male's plumage in summer. **T. torquātus alpestris** (Brehm), alpine ring-ouzel. *Torquatus*, see below. *Alpestris*, mountain-; coined from L. *Alpes*, high mountains; with ref. to the bird's habitat. **T. torquātus torquatus** Linnæus, ring-ouzel. L. *torquatus*, adorned with a collar; *torques*, collar; with ref. to the patch on the bird's throat—white on the male and light brown on the female. **T. viscivorus** Linnæus, mistle-thrush. "Mistletoe-eating"; coined from L. *viscum*, mistletoe, and *voro*, devour; the bird's fondness for these berries was mentioned by Aristotle (617a, 19).

Tyto Billberg. Gr. *tuto*, a kind of owl (Hesychius); imitative of the bird's call (Plautus: *Menæchmi*, 4, 2, 91). **T. alba alba** (Scopoli), white-breasted barn-owl. Fem. of L. *albus*, white; with ref. to the bird's face and under parts. **T. alba guttāta** (Brehm), dark-breasted barn-owl. *Alba*, see above, but this bird is not white at all. *Guttata*, fem. of L. *guttatus*, spotted; *gutta*, a spot; with ref. to the bird's under parts.

Upupa Linnæus. L. *upupa*, hoopoe (Pliny, X, 44); imitative of the bird's call (Varro). **U. epops epops** Linnæus, hoopoe. Gr. *epops*, hoopoe (Aristophanēs: *Birds*, 226); imitative of the bird's call.

Ūria Brisson. Gr. *ouria*, a water-bird almost as large as a duck, of the colour of dirty clay and with a long and narrow bill (Athēnæus, 395d). **U. aalge aalge** (Pontoppidan), northern guillemot. Swedish *alka*, auk. **U. aalge albiōnis** Witherby, southern guillemot. *Aalge*, see above. *Albionis*, gen. of L. *Albion*, England; from *albus*, white, with ref. to England's white cliffs; breeds on cliffs in the British Isles and also in Brittany and N.W. Spain and Portugal. **U. grylle grylle** (Linnæus), black guillemot. Swedish *grissla*, guillemot. **U. lomvia lomvia** (Linnæus), Brünnich's guillemot. Swedish *lomvia*, a kind of guillemot or diver.

Vanellus Brisson. "Little fan"; coined and misspelt dim. of L. *vannus*, a fan (for winnowing); with ref. to the slow, flapping action of the bird's wings in flight. **V. vanellus** (Linnæus), lapwing.

Xema Leach. Coined arbitrarily. **X. sabīni** (Sabine), Sabine's gull. Named by Joseph Sabine after his brother, Captain (later General Sir) Edward Sabine, who discovered the bird on the west coast of Greenland in 1818.

Xenus Kaup. Gr. *xenos*, stranger; perhaps with ref. to its distant migrations—it breeds in N.E. Europe and in Siberia, but winters as far afield as Australia and S. Africa. **X. cinereus** Güldenstädt, Terek sandpiper. L. *cinereus*, ash-coloured; *cinis* (gen. *cineris*), ashes; with ref. to the bird's upper parts in winter.

LIST II: COMMON NAMES

(If any name or part of a name is not explained in this list, consult List I.)

Accentor, Alpine, *Prūnella collāris collaris. Accentor*, anglicized L. word, which used to be the scientific name of this bird's genus; derived from *ad*, towards, and *cano*, sing; the meaning is "one who sings with another" or perhaps here "chorister"; the bird hardly deserves such a complimentary name, though it is a good songster. *Alpine*, breeds high up on mountains, and even in winter mostly frequents mountains, though lower down.

Albatross, Black-browed, *Diomēdea melanophrys. Albatross*, corruption of Portuguese *alcatraz*; from Arabic *al kadoos*, meaning primarily the "trough of an irrigation-wheel," but secondarily a "pelican," on account of the shape of its bill, in which it was believed to carry water to its young. *Al* is the Arabic definite article, and *kadoos* comes from Gr. *kados*, bucket. The initial *alba* in the English name, as contrasted with the *alca* in the Portuguese name, may have arisen from confusion with *alba*, fem. of L. *albus*, white.

Auk. Swedish *alka*, auk. **Great A.,** *Alca impennis*. Extinct. Was about 32 in. long, compared with the little auk's 8 in. **Little A.,** *Alle alle alle*. About 8 in. long, compared with the great auk's 32 in.

Avocet, *Recurvirostra avosetta.*

Bee-eater, *Merops apiaster.*

Bittern, *Botaurus stellāris stellaris*. Fr. *butor*. See under *Botaurus* in List I. **American B.,** *Botaurus lentīginōsus*. Found mostly in N. America. **Little B.,** *Ixobrychus minūtus minutus.*

Blackbird, *Turdus merula merula*. Only the male is black; the female is dark brown.

Blackcap, *Sylvia ātricapilla atricapilla.*

Bluethroat. The name refers mainly to the males of this genus. **Red-spotted B.,** *Luscinia svēcica svecica*. The name refers particularly to the male's plumage in summer, when there is a chestnut patch on the breast in the middle of a blue gorget. **White-spotted B.,** *Luscinia svēcica cyanecula*. The name refers particularly to the male's plumage in summer, when there is a white patch on the breast in the middle of a blue gorget.

Brambling, *Fringilla montifringilla*. The name means the "little bramble-(bird)," and the bird is known also as the "bramble-finch," but woods, not brambles, are its characteristic habitat.

Bullfinch. Probably from the thickness of its head and neck. **British B.,** *Pyrrhūla pyrrhula nesa*. Confined to the British Isles. **Northern B.,** *Pyrrhūla pyrrhula pyrrhula*. Found mostly in N. Europe.

Bunting. The origin of the name is uncertain, but possibly the name is derived from or cognate with German *bunt*, which means, among other things, "mottled"—an epithet which is true at any rate of the corn-bunting, which used to be known simply as the "bunting." **Black-headed B.,** *Emberīza melanocephala*. **Cirl B.,** *Emberīza cirlus cirlus*. **Corn-B.,** *Emberīza calandra*. From its partiality for cultivated land. **Lapland B.,** *Calcārius lappōnicus lapponicus*. **Little B.,** *Emberīza pusilla*. **Meadow-B., East Siberian,** *Emberīza cioidēs castaneīceps. Meadow*, not a very suitable name, though open grassy hills form one of its habitats. *Eastern Siberian*, "Eastern Asiatic" would be a more appropriate name. **Ortolan B.,** *Emberīza hortulāna*. From L. *hortulanus*; which see in List I. **Pine-B.,** *Emberīza leucocephala*. An inappropriate name, though the bird is sometimes found in conifer forests during the breeding-season. **Red-headed B.**, *Emberīza brūniceps.* **Reed-B.**, *Emberīza schœniclus schœniclus.* **Reed-B.**, **Large-billed, Eastern,** *Emberīza schœniclus tschusii.* *Large-billed,* refers to the thickness and depth of the bill, rather than its length. *Eastern,* that is, Eastern Europe; found mostly on the Lower Danube. **Reed-B.**, **Large-billed, Western,** *Emberīza schœniclus compīlātor.* *Large-billed,* see above. *Western,* that is, Western compared with the Eastern form; the Western form is mostly confined to Italy. **Rock-B.**, *Emberīza cia cia.* Rocky ground is its favourite habitat. **Rustic B.**, *Emberīza rustica.* **Snow-B.**, *Plēctrophenax nivālis nivalis.* **Yellow B.**, *Emberīza citrinella citrinella.* **Yellow-breasted B.**, *Emberīza aureola.*

Bustard. Corruption of O.Fr. *bistarde*, which itself comes from L. *avis tarda; avis* means "bird," and as far back as Albertus Magnus it has been assumed that *tarda* is the fem. of *tardus,* slow; but it is clear from Pliny (X, 29) that *tarda* in this context is not a L. word at all, but came from Spain, and it may well have been a noun and not an adjective; its derivation, however, is unknown. **Great B.**, *Ōtis tarda tarda.* The male is about 40 in. long, compared with the little bustard's 17 in. **Little B., Eastern,** *Ōtis tetrax orientālis.* The male is about 17 in. long, compared with the great bustard's 40 in. **Little B., Western,** *Ōtis tetrax tetrax. Little,* see above. *Western,* breeds in S.W. Europe and N.W. Africa. **Macqueen's B.**, *Chlamydōtis undulāta macqueenii.*

Buzzard. Fr. *busard;* which itself comes from L. *buteo,* buzzard (Pliny X, 9). **Common B.**, *Būteo buteo buteo.* **Honey-B.**, *Pernis apivorus apivorus.* **Rough-legged B.**, *Būteo lagōpus lagopus.* **Steppe-B.**, *Būteo buteo vulpīnus.* The Russian steppes constitute one of the places where the bird breeds.

Capercaillie, *Tetraö ūrogallus urogallus.* Of Gaelic origin. It is agreed that *caillie* represents *coille,* gen. of *coll,* and means

"of the wood"; but opinions differ about the derivation of *caper.* The most common explanation is that it comes from *capull,* horse, with ref. to the bird's great size; and this is supported by Gesner, who says the name means *sylvestrēs equi,* which is L. for "horses of the wood." Some authorities, however, prefer *cabher,* old man, used figuratively for "old bird"; and others *gabur,* goat, with ref. to the male's beard-like chin-feathers.

Chaffinch. From its habit of searching chaff for seeds. **British C.**, *Fringilla cœlebs gengleri.* Confined to the British Isles. **Continental C.**, *Fringilla cœlebs cœlebs.* Breeds on the continent of Europe and in W. Siberia.

Chiffchaff, *Phylloscopus collybita collybita.* Imitative of the bird's call. **Scandinavian C.**, *Phylloscopus collybita abietīnus.* Breeds in Scandinavia, but also in many other places. **Siberian C.**, *Phylloscopus collybita tristis.* Breeds in Siberia and E. Russia.

Chough, *Pyrrhocorax pyrrhocorax pyrrhocorax.* A.-S. *ceo,* jackdaw, chough; imitative of the bird's call.

Coot, *Fulica ātra atra.* Apparently of Celtic origin; cf. Welsh *cwtiar,* coot, lit. "bob-tailed hen"; *cwt,* short, and *iar,* hen.

Cormorant, *Phalacrocorax carbo carbo.* Fr. *cormoran;* which itself comes from L. *corvus marīnus,* lit. "sea-crow"; *corvus,* crow, and *marinus,* sea-. **Southern C.**, *Phalacrocorax carbo sinensis.* Breeds as far south as India and not further north than middle Europe, whereas the (common) cormorant breeds mainly in N. Europe.

Courser, Cream-coloured, *Cursōrius cursor cursor.* Mostly of a sandy-buff colour, apart from its wings, which are mainly black.

Crake. Cognate with Gr. and L. *crex;* imitative of the bird's call. **Baillon's C.**, *Porzāna pusilla intermedia.* After Louis François Antoine Baillon of Abbeville, who discovered the bird in Picardy and gave Vieillot details of its habits; Baillon died about 1855. **Caro-lina C.**, *Porzāna carolīna*. **Corn-C.**, *Crex crex*. In spite of its name the bird is not often found in cornfields. **Little C.**, *Porzāna parva*. **Spotted C.**, *Porzāna porzana*. Has white spots on its breast, neck and back.

Crane, Common, *Grus grus grus*. A.-S. *cran*; imitative of the bird's call.

Creeper. From the bird's habit of climbing in search of insects for food. **Tree-C.**, **British,** *Certhia familiāris britannica*. Climbs trees in search of insects. **Tree-C.**, **Northern,** *Certhia familiāris familiaris*. *Tree*, see above. *Northern*, found mostly in N. Europe. **Wall-C.**, *Tīchodroma mūrāria*.

Crossbill, Common, *Loxia curvirostra curvirostra*. The tips of the bird's mandibles cross each other. **Parrot-C.**, *Loxia pytyopsittacus*. **Scottish C.**, *Loxia curvirostra scōtica*. **Two-barred C.**, *Loxia leucoptera bifasciāta*. **White-winged C.**, **American,** *Loxia leucoptera leucoptera*. Breeds and winters in N. America.

Crow. A.-S. *crawe*; that is, a croaking bird; Aryan root *gar*, cry out. **Carrion-C.**, *Corvus corōnē corone*. Carrion is one of its many kinds of food. **Hooded C.**, *Corvus cornix cornix*. From the hood-like appearance of its grey back.

Cuckoo, *Cucūlus canōrus canorus*. Fr. *coucou*, which itself comes from L. *cuculus*. All languages agree in naming the bird after its call. **Black-billed C.**, *Coccyzus erythrophthalmus*. So called by contrast with the yellow-billed cuckoo, which the black-billed cuckoo resembles in most respects. **Great Spotted C.**, *Clāmātor glandārius*. *Great*, the bird's length is 15½ in., compared with the (common) cuckoo's 13 in. *Spotted*, with ref. to the white spots on the bird's upper parts. **Yellow-billed C.**, *Coccyzus americānus americanus*. So called by contrast with the black-billed cuckoo, which the yellow-billed cuckoo resembles in most respects.

Curlew. O. Fr. *corlieu*; imitative of the bird's call. **Common C.**, *Nūmēnius arquāta arquata*. **Eskimo C.**, *Nūmēnius*

boreālis. Now almost extinct, but used to breed in N. Canada. **Slender-billed C.**, *Nūmēnius tenuirostris*. **Stone-C.**, *Burhīnus œdicnēmus œdicnemus*. Often breeds in stony places.

Dipper. So called either because it "dips" (dives) into the water after its food or because it perches on a stone in the water and keeps on "dipping" as though curtseying. **Black-bellied D.**, *Cinclus cinclus cinclus*. Its belly is almost entirely brownish-black without the chestnut band that borders the front of the British dipper's belly. **British D.**, *Cinclus cinclus gulāris*. Confined to Great Britain. **Irish D.**, *Cinclus cinclus hibernicus*.

Diver. From its great powers of submergence. **Black-throated D.**, *Colymbus arcticus arcticus*. Refers to the summer plumage. **Northern D., Great,** *Colymbus immer*. *Northern*, breeds in Iceland and N. America. *Great*, it is actually smaller than the white-billed northern diver—31 in. long against 33 in. **Northern D., White-billed,** *Colymbus adamsii*. *Northern*, breeds in Iceland and N. America. *White-billed*, its bill is whitish as contrasted with the blackish bill of the great northern diver. **Red-throated D.**, *Colymbus stellātus*. Refers to the bird's summer plumage.

Dotterel, *Eudromias mōrinellus*, that is, "a little fool"; from *dote* and the dim. suffix *-rel*. For the origin of the bird's reputation for stupidity, see under *Eudromias morinellus* in List I.

Dove. Said to be cognate with A.-S. *dufan*, to dive; but the connexion is not clear. **Rock-D.**, *Columba līvia livia*. It mostly frequents rocky coasts. **Stock-D.**, *Columba œnas*. It usually breeds in the stocks of hollow trees. **Turtle-D.**, *Streptopelia turtur turtur*. *Turtle* is derived from L. *turtur*, which see under the scientific name in List I. **Turtle D., Eastern Rufous,** *Streptopelia orientālis orientalis*. *Turtle*, see above. *Rufous*, refers particularly to the bird's mantle.

Duck. M.E. *duke*; from *duken*, to dive.
Buffel-headed D., *Bucephala albeola*.
Buffel, Fr. *buffle*, buffalo; with ref. to the
squatness of the bird's head. **Ferruginous D.**, *Aythya nyroca nyroca*. Chestnut
is its prevailing hue, especially when it is
in the water and the white of its under
parts is hidden. **Harlequin-D.**, *Histriōnicus histrionicus histrionicus*. The
common name has been taken from the
scientific, which see in List I. **Long-
tailed D.**, *Clangula hyemālis*. Refers to
the male, whose central tail-feathers
project about 5 in. beyond the others
(except during its moult). **Scaup-D.**,
Aythya marīla marila. Scaup is cognate
with *scallop* and *scalp*, and originally
meant a "shell"; the bird is so called
because it feeds among mussel shells.
Sheld-D., *Tadorna tadorna*. *Sheld* is
M.E. for "variegated", the bird's plumage being a mixture of black, white,
chestnut and metallic green. **Sheld-D.**,
Ruddy, *Casarca ferrūginea*. **Tufted D.**,
Aythya fūlīgula. Refers to the male's
drooping crest.

Dunlin. Probably from *dune*, sand
mound, and *-ling*, creature; sand being
a common habitat of the bird outside
the breeding-season. Some authorities
derive the name from the colour *dun*
and the dim. suffix *-ling*; but the
description seems inappropriate for a
bird with so much grey in its plumage.
Northern D., *Calidris alpīna alpina*.
Breeds in N. Europe and the arctic
region. **Southern D.**, *Calidris alpīna
schinzii*. Breeds in N. Europe, but
mostly south of the northern race's
region.

Eagle. Fr. *aigle*, which itself comes from
L. *aquila*. **Golden E.**, *Aquila chrȳsaëtus
chrysaetus*. **Spotted E.**, *Aquila clanga*.
Refers to its immature plumage, which
has whitish or buff spots; it is mostly
immature birds that find their way to
Britain. **White-tailed E.**, *Haliaëtus
albicilla*.

Egret, Little, *Egretta garzetta garzetta*.
That is, little as compared with the great
white heron, which is also included in

the genus *Egretta*—21 in. long against
35 in.
Eider. Icelandic *ædr*. **Common E.**,
Sōmateria mollissima mollissima. **King-
E.**, *Sōmateria spectābilis*. Presumably
from its showy appearance, though it
is rather smaller than the common eider.
Steller's E., *Polysticta stelleri*.

Falcon. O.Fr. *faulcon*, from L. *falco*.
Greenland F., *Falco rusticolus candicans*.
Breeds mainly in Greenland. **Gyr-F.**,
Falco rusticolus rusticolus. M.L. *gyrofalco*;
the *gyro*, according to Albertus Magnus,
is derived from L. *gyro*, to circle; with
ref. to the bird's habit of circling a long
time before swooping on its prey.
Iceland F., *Falco rusticolus islandus*.
Peregrine F., *Falco peregrīnus peregrinus*.
Peregrine F., **North American,** *Falco
peregrīnus anatum*. Breeds and winters
in N. America. **Red-footed F.**, *Falco
vespertīnus vespertinus*. Has orange-red
legs, as contrasted with the yellow legs
of most falcons.

Fieldfare, *Turdus pilāris*. From the A.-S.;
fare comes from *faran*, to fare, travel;
field comes either from *feld*, field, or
fealo, fallow-land; in winter the bird
mainly frequents open country.

Finch. A.-S. *finc*. **Bullf.** See "Bull-
finch." **Chaff.** See "Chaffinch."
Citril F., *Carduēlis citrinella citrinella*.
Citril is a shortened form of *citrinella*.
Greenf. See "Greenfinch." **Goldf.**
See "Goldfinch." **Hawf.** See "Haw-
finch." **Snow-F.**, *Montifringilla nivālis
nivalis*.

Firecrest, *Rēgulus ignicapillus ignicapillus*.

Flamingo, *Phœnīcopterus ruber roseus*.
Spanish *flamenco*; ultimately from L.
flamma, flame; with ref. to the flame-
coloured patch on the bird's wings.

Flycatcher. Its chief food is flies of
various kinds, which are taken on the
wing. **Brown F.**, *Muscicapa lātirostris*.
Brown is the prevailing colour of the
whole bird. **Collared F.**, *Muscicapa
albicollis*. Refers to the male's white
collar. **Pied F.**, *Muscicapa hypoleuca
hypoleuca*. Refers to the male's summer
plumage, which is white below and

black above with white forehead and white bar on the wings. **Red-breasted F.**, *Muscicapa parva parva.* Refers to the male's red throat and upper breast. **Spotted F.**, *Muscicapa striāta striata.* The adults are not really spotted, but have stripes on their head and breast; in the immature birds the markings are more like spots.

Gadwall, *Anas strepera.* No plausible derivation of this name has ever been given. Perhaps it is connected with A.-S. *gad*, a point; with ref. to the fine tooth-like projections on the edges of the bird's mandibles.

Gannet, *Sula bassāna.* A.-S. *ganot*; cognate with *gander*; both come from the Aryan root *gha*, to gape.

Garganey, *Anas querquedula.* Taken from Gesner, who gave this as the Italian name used round Bellinzona (Switzerland) and Lake Maggiore (Lombardy, N. Italy).

Godwit. Said to be derived from A.-S. *god wiht*, good creature; perhaps with ref. to its being good to eat. **Bartailed G.**, *Līmōsa lappōnica lapponica.* Its tail is usually marked with brown and greyish bars, but they are not conspicuous. **Black-tailed G.**, *Līmosa limosa limosa.* The main part of its tail is actually white, but at the tip there is a broad black band.

Goldcrest. The name applies to the female; the male's crest is orange. **British G.**, *Rēgulus regulus anglōrum.* **Continental G.**, *Rēgulus regulus regulus.* Found mostly on the continent of Europe.

Goldeneye, *Bucephala clangula clangula.* From the colour of its irises.

Goldfinch, from the broad gold band on its wings. **British G.**, *Carduēlis carduelis britannica.* **Continental G.**, *Carduēlis carduelis carduelis.* Found mostly on the continent of Europe.

Goosander, *Mergus merganser merganser.* The name may mean "goose-duck," *ander* being the plural of Norwegian *and*, duck; if so, the ref. is to the bird's large

size, this bird being the largest of all species of ducks.

Goose. A.-S. *gos*; probably from the Aryan root *gha*, to gape. **Barnacle-G.**, *Branta leucopsis.* There is a legend that this bird springs from the shell-fish known as a barnacle; but according to *The Oxford English Dictionary* "all the evidence shows that the name was originally applied to the bird which had the marvellous origin, not to the shell which, according to some, produced it." The M.E. name was *bernekke*, possibly with ref. to the "burnt" (that is, black, charred) appearance of the bird's neck; cf. the meaning of "brent" goose. **Bean-G.**, *Anser fabālis fabalis.* **Brent G., Dark-breasted,** *Branta bernicla bernicla.* Several explanations of *brent* have been offered, the most probable perhaps being that it is cognate with the German name *brand(gans)*, lit. "burned (goose)," with ref. to the black, charred appearance of much of the bird's plumage. *Dark-breasted*, refers to the lower part of the breast, which is not much paler than the bird's upper parts. **Brent G., Pale-breasted,** *Branta bernicla hrota.* Brent, see above. *Pale-breasted*, refers to the lower part of the breast, which is considerably paler than the bird's upper parts. **Canada G.**, *Branta canadensis canadensis.* **Grey Lag-G.**, *Anser anser anser.* Grey, its prevailing colour is greyish-brown. *Lag*, the derivation is obscure; according to Skeat the meaning is the goose that "lags" behind, that is, the goose that used to stay on in England after the other kinds had gone away to breed. **Pink-footed G.**, *Anser fabālis brachyrhynchus.* **Red-breasted G.**, *Branta rūficollis.* The upper part of its breast and also its neck are chestnut. **Snow-G.**, *Anser hyperboreus hyperboreus.* From its colour and habitat. **Snow-G., Greater,** *Anser hyperboreus atlanticus.* Snow, see above. *Greater*, its length is about 30 in., compared with the (common) snow-goose's 25–28 in. **White-fronted G.**, *Anser albifrons albifrons.* **White-fronted G., Lesser,** *Anser erythropus.* *White-fronted*, with ref. to the white patch at the base of the bird's bill in front of its head. *Lesser*, its length is about 21-26 in., compared with the (common) white-fronted goose's 26-30 in.

Goshawk, *Accipiter gentīlis gentilis*, that is, "goose-hawk"; A.-S. *gos*, goose; geese are one of the many kinds of creatures on which this hawk preys. **American G.,** *Accipiter gentīlis ātricapillus*. Found mostly in N. America.

Grebe. Fr. *grèbe*, which itself comes from Breton *krib*, comb, crest; with ref. to the crest of some species. **Black-necked G.,** *Pōdiceps nigricollis nigricollis*. **Great Crested G.,** *Pōdiceps cristātus cristatus*. Its length is about 19 in., compared with the little grebe's 10½ in. **Little G.,** *Pōdiceps rūficollis ruficollis*. Its length is about 10½ in., compared with the great crested grebe's 19 in. **Red-necked G.,** *Pōdiceps griseïgena griseigena*. Refers to its summer plumage, when the front and sides of the neck are chestnut. **Red-necked G., American,** *Pōdiceps griseïgena holboellii*. *Red-necked*, see above. *American*, breeds and winters in N. America, but also found in Asia. **Slavonian G.,** *Pōdiceps aurītus*. The bird breeds in N. Europe, N. Asia and N. America.

Greenfinch, *Chlōris chloris chloris*.

Greenshank, *Tringa nebulāria*. From its olive-green legs.

Grosbeak, Fr. *grosbec*, lit. "thick-beak"; the name is appropriate. **Pine-G.,** *Pīnicola ēnucleātor enucleator*. **Scarlet G.,** *Carpodacus erythrīnus erythrinus*.

Grouse. Perhaps from O.Fr. *griesche*, grey, speckled. **Black G., British,** *Lyrūrus tetrix britannicus*. *Black*, refers to the male's plumage. **Red G., British,** *Lagōpus scōticus scoticus*. *Red*, generally speaking, the plumage is red-brown. *British*, the bird was originally confined to Great Britain, but has been introduced into the western part of the continent of Europe. **Red G., Irish,** *Lagōpus scōticus hibernicus*. *Red*, see above. **Sand-G., Pallas's,** *Syrrhaptēs paradoxus*. *Sand-*, from its usual habitat. *Pallas's*, after the German naturalist and traveller, Peter Simon Pallas (1741-1811), who dis-

covered the bird in the Tartary desert in 1773.

Guillemot. The Fr. name, which is itself probably derived from *Guillaume*, William; cf. the Norfolk names for this bird, *willock* and *willy*, and the similar nicknames *magpie, robin, martin, jenny wren*. **Black G.,** *Ūria grylle grylle*. Refers to the summer plumage. **Brunnich's G.,** *Ūria lomvia lomvia*. After the Danish ornithologist who published *Ornīthologia Boreālis* ("Northern Ornithology") in 1764. **Northern G.,** *Ūria aalge aalge*. Breeds in N. Europe and northern part of N. America. **Southern G.,** *Ūria aalge albiōnis*. Breeds off Brittany and N.W. Spain and Portugal.

Gull. Cornish *gullan*; probably imitative of the bird's call, cf. Breton *goelaff*, weep. **Black-backed G., Great,** *Larus marīnus*. *Great*, about 25-27 in. long, compared with the British lesser black-backed gull's 21 in. **Black-backed G., Lesser, British,** *Larus fuscus grællsii*. *Lesser*, about 21 in. long, compared with the great black-backed gull's 25-27 in. *British*, breeds mainly in the British Isles. **Black-backed G., Lesser, Scandinavian,** *Larus fuscus fuscus*. *Lesser*, see above. *Scandinavian*, breeds in Scandinavia and other parts of N. Europe. **Black-headed G.,** *Larus rīdibundus ridibundus*. Refers to the chocolate-brown hood of its summer plumage. **Black-headed G., Great,** *Larus ichthyaëtus*. *Black-headed*, the hood is really black in summer, not brown like that of the (common) black-headed gull. *Great*, about 25 in. long, compared with the (common) black-headed gull's 14-15 in. **Black-headed G., Mediterranean,** *Larus melanocephalus*. *Black-headed*, as for the great black-headed gull. *Mediterranean*, breeds and winters mainly round the Mediterranean. **Bonaparte's G.,** *Larus philadephia*. After the Italian ornithologist, Prince Charles Bonaparte of Canino (1803-1857). **Common G.,** *Larus cānus canus*. A misnomer, the most common gull being the black-headed one. **Glaucous G.,** *Larus hyperboreus*. Refers to the adult's pale grey mantle. **Herring-G.,** *Larus argentātus argentatus,* that is, "herring-eating," though actually herrings form only a small part of its diet. **Herring-G., Scandinavian,** *Larus argentātus omissus. Herring-,* see above. *Scandinavian,* breeds mainly in Scandinavia. **Iceland G.,** *Larus glaucoidēs.* A misnomer; Greenland is the only place where the bird is definitely known to breed. **Ivory-G.,** *Pagophila eburnea.* **Little G.,** *Larus minūtus.* **Ross's G.,** *Rhodostēthia rosea.* After Sir John Ross, British rear-admiral and arctic explorer, who discovered the bird (1777–1856). **Sabine's G.,** *Xema sabīni.*

Harrier. So called from its "harrying" or destroying other creatures, particularly poultry. **Hen-.,** *Circus cyaneus cyaneus.* Occasionally kills a chicken, but that is only one of the many kinds of creatures on which it preys. **Marsh-.,** *Circus ærūginōsus æruginosus.* From its usual haunt. **Montagu's H.,** *Circus pygargus.* After the British ornithologist, Col. George Montagu (1751–1815). **Pallid H.,** *Circus macrourus.* Refers to the pale grey plumage of the adult male.

Hawfinch, *Coccothraustēs coccothraustes coccothraustes.* Feeds mainly on kernels and seeds, including haw seeds.

Hawk, Sparrow-, *Accipiter nīsus nisus. Hawk,* A.-S. *hafoc,* cognate with A.-S. *habban,* seize, hold; with ref. to the bird's predatory habit. *Sparrow-,* because the sparrow is one of the birds that form the prey of this kind of hawk.

Heron. O.Fr. *hairon.* **Buff-backed H.,** *Ardeola ibis ibis.* Refers to the summer plumage. **Common H.,** *Ardea cinerea cinerea.* The only heron that is common in the British Isles. **Night-H.,** *Nycticorax nycticorax nycticorax.* **Purple H.,** *Ardea purpurea purpurea.* **Squacco H.,** *Ardeola ralloides.* Misspelling of provincial Italian *sguacco;* probably imitative of the bird's call. **White H., Great,** *Egretta alba alba.* Its length is about 35 in. which is greater than that of any other British heron except the common one, whose length is about 36 in.

Hobby, *Falco subbūteo subbuteo.* Fr. *hoberau,* which itself comes from O.Fr. *hober,* to move (intransitive); with ref. to the bird's activity when hunting.

Hoopoe, *Upupa epops epops.* L. *upupa.*

Ibis, Glossy, *Plēgadis falcinellus falcinellus. Ibis,* the L. name (Pliny, VIII, 41). *Glossy,* refers particularly to the summer plumage.

Jackdaw, *Corvus monēdula spermologus. Jack,* either a nickname on the analogy of *magpie* and *robin* or used as a dim., cf. *jack-snipe. Daw,* O. Low German *daha;* imitative of the bird's call. **Scandinavian J.,** *Corvus monēdula monedula.* Mainly found in Scandinavia.

Jay. O.Fr. *jay;* cognate with E. *gay;* with ref. to the bird's bright plumage. **British J.,** *Garrulus glandārius rūfitergum.* Confined to the British Isles. **Continental J.,** *Garrulus glandārius glandarius.* Breeds on the continent of Europe. **Irish J.,** *Garrulus glandārius hibernicus.*

Kestrel, *Falco tinnunculus tinnunculus.* O.Fr. *quercerelle,* which itself is said to come from L. *querquedula,* a kind of teal; but if that view is correct, it is not known how the name came to be transferred. **Lesser K.,** *Falco naumanni naumanni.* Its length is about 12 in., compared with the (common) kestrel's 13–14 in.

Kingfisher, *Alcēdo atthis ispida.* So called from its skill at catching fish.

Kite, *Milvus milvus milvus.* A.-S. *cyta;* probably from the Aryan root *skut,* to shoot, go swiftly; with ref. to the way in which the bird swoops on its prey, though it is really rather a slow bird-of-prey. **Black K.,** *Milvus migrans migrans.* Darker than the (common) kite, but dark brown, not black.

Kittiwake, *Rissa tridactyla tridactyla.* Imitative of the bird's call.

Knot, *Calidris canūtus canutus.* See under the scientific name in List I.

Lapwing, *Vanellus vanellus.* A.-S. *hleapewince*; lit. "one who turns about in running or flight"; *hleapan*, to run, and *wincian*, lit. "to wink"; with ref. to the male's twisting nuptial flight.

Lark. A.-S. *lawerce*; ultimate derivation unknown. **Black L.,** *Melanocorypha yeltoniensis.* Refers particularly to the male's plumage in summer, which is jet black; in the winter the male's plumage appears much lighter on account of the buff fringes on the feathers; the female's plumage is brown and white. **Calandra L.** *Melanocorypha calandra calandra.* **Crested L.,** *Galērīda cristāta cristata.* **Shore-L.,** *Erēmophila alpestris flāva.* In winter it particularly frequents the sea-shore. **Short-toed L.,** *Calandrella brachydactyla brachydactyla.* **Short-toed L., Eastern,** *Calandrella brachydactyla longipennis.* Found in E. Europe and W. Asia. **Sky-L.,** *Alauda arvensis arvensis.* From its habit of ascending into the sky when singing. **Sky-L., Eastern,** *Alauda arvensis intermedia. Sky,* see above. *Eastern,* breeds in Asia. **White-winged L.,** *Melanocorypha leucoptera.* **Wood-L.,** *Lullula arborea arborea.* Actually it frequents scattered trees, rather than woods.

Linnet, *Carduēlis cannabina cannabina.* Fr. *linotte,* which itself comes from L. *linum,* flax; with ref. to the bird's partiality for seeds of that plant, though in the British Isles it feeds mainly on weeds.

Magpie, *Pīca pica pica. Mag,* short for *Margaret;* for similar nicknames cf. *robin, martin, Jenny wren. Pie,* Fr. *pie,* which itself comes from L. *pica;* probably imitative of the bird's call and cognate with L. *pīpio,* to chirp.

Mallard, *Anas platyrhyncha platyrhyncha.* O.Fr. *malard;* perhaps from O.Fr. *mâle,* male, and suffix *-ard,* used for forming masculine nouns; originally applied to the drake alone, which was probably styled *the* male duck because it is the most common kind of wild duck.

Martin. A nickname; cf. *robin, magpie, Jenny wren.* **House-M.,** *Delichon urbica urbica.* So called because it nests under overhanging eaves of houses. **Sand-M.,** *Rīpāria riparia riparia.* So called because it nests in sand-banks.

Merganser. See under *Mergus merganser merganser* in List I. **Hooded M.,** *Mergus cucullātus.* **Red-brested M.,** *Mergus serrātor.* Refers to the male's chestnut breast.

Merlin, *Falco columbārius æsalon.* O.Fr. *émerillon.*

Moorhen, *Gallīnula chlōropus chloropus. Moor,* A.-S. *mor,* marsh; with ref. to the bird's habitat.

Nightingale, *Luscinia megarhyncha megarhyncha.* A.-S. *nihtigale,* lit. "night-singer"; *nihte,* gen. of *niht,* night, and *gale,* singer. **Thrush-N.,** *Luscinia luscinia.* Refers to the faint thrush-like spots on its breast.

Nightjar, *Caprimulgus europæus europæus. Night,* because it hunts in the evening. *Jar,* refers to the bird's rattle-like call. **Algerian red-necked N.,** *Caprimulgus rūficollis dēsertōrum.* Breeds in Algeria and Tunisia. **American N.,** *Chordeilēs minor minor.* Breeds in N. America, winters in Central and S. America. **Egyptian N.,** *Caprimulgus ægyptius ægyptius.*

Nutcracker. See under *Nucifraga* in List I. **Slender-billed N.,** *Nucifraga caryocatactēs macrorhynchus.* Its bill is more slender than the thick-billed nutcracker's. **Thick-billed N.,** *Nucifraga caryocatactēs caryocatactes.* Its bill is thicker than the slender-billed nutcracker's.

Nuthatch, British, *Sitta europæa affinis. Nuthatch,* that is, nut-hacker; with ref. to its habit of fixing nuts in a crevice of the bark of a tree and then hacking them open with its bill. *British,* confined to Great Britain.

Oriole, Golden, *Oriolus oriolus oriolus. Golden,* see under *Oriolus* in List I.

Osprey, *Pandīōn haliaëtus haliaetus.* Said to be a corruption of L. *ossifraga* (Pliny,

X, 3), lit. "bone-breaker," from *os*
(gen. *ossis*), bone, and *frango*, break. If
that derivation is correct, the name is
inappropriate for the osprey, as it feeds
mostly on fish. The bird meant by
Pliny was the lammergeyer (lit. "lamb-
vulture") or bearded vulture, and
obtained its name of *ossifraga* from its
habit of dropping large bones from a
great height, in order to break them
before feeding on them; but how the
name came to be transferred to the
osprey is not known.

Owl. A.-S. *ule*; cognate with L. *ulula*,
screech-owl (Pliny, X, 16); imitative
of the bird's call. **Barn-O., Dark-
breasted,** *Tyto alba guttāta*. *Barn*,
roosts during day in barns, among
other places. *Dark-breasted*, the bird's
breast is buff, as contrasted with that of
the white-breasted bird. **Barn-O.,
White-breasted,** *Tyto alba alba*. *Barn*,
see above. **Eagle-O.,** *Būbo bubo bubo*.
From its great size and supposed resemblance to an eagle. **Hawk-O., American,** *Surnia ulula caparoch*. *Hawk*, the
bird resembles a hawk in the smallness
of its head, its habit of hunting by day
and its appearance when flying. *American*,
found mainly in Canada. **Hawk-O.,
European,** *Surnia ulula ulula*. *Hawk*,
see above. *European*, found mainly in
Europe. **Little O.,** *Athēnē noctua vidalii*.
Its length is 8½–9 in., compared with the
British tawny owl's 15 in. **Long-eared
O.,** *Asio ōtus otus*. **Scops-O.,** *Otus
scōps scops*. **Short-eared O.,** *Asio
flammeus flammeus*. Its ear tufts are
hardly visible. **Snowy O.,** *Nyctea
scandiāca*. So called because it breeds in
the arctic region and has snow-white
plumage (with brown bars). **Tawny
O., British,** *Strix aluco sylvātica*. *Tawny*,
from its prevailing colour. *British*,
confined to Great Britain. **Tengmalm's
O.,** *Ægolius funereus funereus*. After the
Swedish ornithologist, Peter Gustavus
Tengmalm, who first described the bird
in 1783.

Oyster-catcher, British, *Hæmatopus
ostralegus occidentālis*. *Oyster-catcher*,
actually the bird feeds mainly on

mussels. *British*, by no means confined
to the British Isles, but some birds breed
in them and many birds visit them.

Partridge. Fr. *perdrix*; ultimately from
Gr. *perdix*; see under *Perdix* in List I.
Common P., *Perdix perdix perdix*.
Red-legged P., *Alectoris rūfa rufa*.

Petrel, Fr. *pétrel*, dim. of *Pêtre*, Peter;
after the apostle, whose exploit of walking on the Sea of Galilee the bird seems
to be emulating, as it skims the water
with its feet dangling down. **Bulwer's
P.,** *Bulweria bulwerii*. **Capped P.,**
Pterodroma hasitāta. Has a brown cap.
Collared P., *Pterodroma leucoptera
brevipes*. Most of these birds have a
grey collar-like band on a white breast,
though some birds have the whole
breast grey. **Fork-tailed P., Leach's,**
Ōceănodroma leucorrhoä leucorrhoa. *Fork-
tailed*, this bird's tail resembles that of a
house-martin. *Leach's*, after the British
ornithologist, William Elford Leach
(1790–1836), who acquired the typical
specimen. **Fork-tailed P., Madeiran,**
Ōceănodroma castro. *Fork-tailed*, see
above. *Madeiran*, from one of its main
breeding-places. **Frigate-P.,** *Pelagodroma marīna hypoleuca*. So called from
its swift flight. **Fulmar P.,** *Fulmārus
glaciālis glacialis*. Perhaps from O. Norse
ful, foul, and *ma*, mew, gull; with ref.
to the smell of the oil which the bird
emits when molested. **Kermadec P.,**
Pterodroma neglecta. Breeds particularly
on the Kermadec Islands (N.N.E. of New
Zealand). **Storm-P.,** *Hydrobatēs pelagicus*. Believed by sailors to be the
harbinger of a storm. **Wilson's P.,**
Ōceănītēs oceanicus. After the American
ornithologist, Alexander Wilson (1766–
1813), who first figured the bird.

Phalarope, Grey, *Phalāropus fulicārius*.
Refers to the winter plumage, when the
prevailing colours are grey and white;
in summer the prevailing colour is
reddish-brown. **Red-necked P.,**
Phalāropus lobātus. Refers to the summer
plumage, when there is a reddish band
on the neck.

Pheasant, *Phāsiānus colchicus*. Fr. *faisan*; ultimately from Gr. *phasianos*; see under *Phasianus* in List I.

Pigeon, Wood-, *Columba palumbus palumbus*. *Pigeon*, Fr. *pigeon*; ultimately from the imitative L. *pīpio*, to chirp. *Wood-*, from the bird's favourite habitat.

Pintail, *Anas acūta acuta*. From its long pointed tail.

Pipit. Fr. *pipit*; ultimately from the imitative L. *pīpio*, to chirp. **Meadow-P.,** *Anthus prātensis*. **Petchora P.,** *Anthus gustāvi*. Found particularly in the lower valley of the River Petchora, N.E. Russia. **Red-throated P.,** *Anthus cervīnus*. Refers to the summer plumage. **Richard's P.,** *Anthus richardi richardi*. **Rock-P.,** *Anthus spīnoletta petrōsus*. **Rock-P., Hebridean,** *Anthus spīnoletta meinertzhāgeni*. **Rock-,** breeds mainly on rocky coasts and islands. *Hebridean*, found particularly in the Outer Hebrides. **Rock-P., Scandinavian,** *Anthus spīnoletta littorālis*. *Rock-*, see above. *Scandinavian*, breeds mainly in Scandinavia. **Tawny P.,** *Anthus campestris campestris*. Its plumage is brownish of various shades. **Tree-P.,** *Anthus triviālis trivialis*. Frequents scattered trees, not woods. **Water-P.,** *Anthus spīnoletta spinoletta*. Usually found near water. **Water-P., American,** *Anthus spīnoletta rubescens*. *Water-*, see above. *American*, found mostly in N. America.

Plover. Fr. *pluvier*; ultimately from L. *pluvia*, rain. See under *Pluvialis* in List I. **Caspian P.,** *Eupoda asiātica asiatica*. Breeds particularly round the Caspian Sea. **Golden P., American,** *Pluvialis dominica dominica*. *Golden*, with ref. to the yellow markings on its upper plumage, particularly in the summer. *American*, breeds in N. America, winters in S. America. **Golden P., Asiatic,** *Pluvialis dominica fulva*. *Golden*, see above. *Asiatic*, breeds mainly in N. Siberia. **Golden P., Northern,** *Pluvialis aprīcāria altifrons*. *Golden*, see under "American Golden Plover." *Northern*, breeds in extreme north of Europe. **Golden P., Southern,** *Pluvialis aprīcāria apricaria*. *Golden*, see under "American Golden Plover." *Southern*,

breeds in N. Europe, but more south than the northern golden plover. **Grey P.,** *Squātarōla squatarola*. Refers to the markings on its upper plumage. **Kentish P.,** *Leucopolius alexandrīnus alexandrinus*. Used to breed round Dungeness. **Killdeer P.,** *Oxyēchus vociferus vociferus*. Supposed to be imitative of the bird's call. **Ringed P.,** *Charadrius hiāticula hiaticula*. From the black collar that separates the bird's white throat from its white breast. **Ringed P., Arctic,** *Charadrius hiāticula tundræ*. *Ringed*, see above. *Arctic*, breeds in the arctic region and the extreme north of Europe. **Ringed P., Little,** *Charadrius dubius cūronīcus*. *Ringed*, see under (Common) "Plover, Ringed." *Little*, 6 in. long, compared with the (common) ringed plover's 7½ in. **Ringed P., Semi-palmated,** *Charadrius hiāticula semi-palmātus*. *Ringed*, see under (Common) "Plover, Ringed." **Sociable P.,** *Chettūsia gregāria*.

Pochard. No plausible derivation of the name is forthcoming. **Common P.,** *Aythya ferīna*. **Red-crested P.,** *Nētta rūfīna*. Refers to the male, though its whole head is reddish.

Pratincole, *Glāreola prātincola pratincola*. **Black-winged P.,** *Glāreola nordmanni*. Refers to the under part of its wings, which is black in contrast with the (common) pratincole's chestnut.

Ptarmigan, Scottish, *Lagōpus mūtus millaisi*. *Ptarmigan*, Gaelic *tarmachan*, but the derivation of the Gaelic word is unknown. *Scottish*, confined to Scotland.

Puffin, Southern, *Frātercula arctica grābæ*. *Puffin*, from the puffed-out appearance of its body and bill. *Southern*, breeds in places ranging from the Færoes to Brittany, and winters as far south as the Canaries.

Quail, *Coturnix coturnix coturnix*. O.Fr. *quaille*; cognate with *quack*; imitative of the bird's call.

Rail, Water-, *Rallus aquāticus aquaticus*. Fr. *râle*; cognate with E. *rattle*; imitative of the bird's call.

Raven, *Corvus corax corax.* A.-S. *hræfn*; imitative of the bird's call.

Razorbill. Refers to the shape of its deep, laterally compressed bill. **British R.,** *Alca torda britannica.* **Northern R.,** *Alca torda torda.* Breeds in N. Europe and the northern part of N. America.

Redpoll. Refers to its crimson forehead. **Coues's R.,** *Carduēlis hornemanni exīlipes.* After the American ornithologist, Elliott Coues (1842–1899). **Greenland R.,** *Carduēlis flammea rostrāta.* Occurs mostly in Greenland. **Hollböll's R.,** *Carduēlis flammea holboellii.* **Hornemann's R.,** *Carduēlis hornemanni hornemanni.* **Lesser R.,** *Carduēlis flammea cabaret.* About 4¾ in. long, compared with the mealy redpoll's 5 in. **Mealy R.,** *Carduēlis flammea flammea.* That is, pale; the bird being paler than the lesser redpoll.

Redshank. From its orange-red legs. **British R.,** *Tringa totanus britannica.* **Continental R.,** *Tringa totanus totanus.* Breeds on the continent of Europe and in parts of Asia. **Iceland R.,** *Tringa totanus rōbusta.* Breeds mainly in Iceland. **Spotted R.,** *Totanus erythropus.* Refers particularly to its plumage in summer, when the black back is marked with white spots.

Redstart, *Phœnicūrus phœnicurus phœnicurus.* *Start* comes from A.-S. *steort*, tail; the bird's tail is orange-chestnut. **Black R.,** *Phœnicūrus ōchrūrus gibraltāriensis.* Refers to the male's plumage in summer, when the throat and breast are black and the back dark grey.

Redwing, *Turdus musicus musicus.* The noticeably red part of the bird is not its wings, but its flanks and axillaries. **Iceland R.,** *Turdus musicus coburni.* Breeds mainly in Iceland.

Ring-ouzel, *Turdus torquātus torquatus.* *Ring*, the male has a white gorget, the female a brownish one. *Ouzel*, A.-S. *osle*, blackbird. **Alpine R.,** *Turdus torquātus alpestris.*

Robin. Originally "Robin Redbreast," *robin* being a nickname; cf. *magpie*, *martin*, *Jenny wren*. **British R.,** *Erithacus rubecula melophilus.* Breeds mainly in the British Isles. **Continental R.,** *Erithacus rubecula rubecula.* Breeds solely on the European continent.

Roller, *Coracias garrulus garrulus.* According to Gesner this was the name used round Strasbourg in imitation of the bird's call, but it is more likely to be derived from German *rollen*, to roll, with ref. to the male's habit of "rolling" or turning over in its nuptial flight.

Rook, *Corvus frugilegus frugilegus.* A.-S. *hroc*; imitative of the bird's call.

Ruff, *Philomachus pugnax.* So called from the male's conspicuous ruff in the breeding-season.

Sanderling, *Crocēthia alba.* Icelandic *sanderla*, which itself comes from *sand*, sand, and *erla*, wagtail; outside the breeding-season the bird's favourite habitat is sandy shores.

Sandpiper. *Sand*, from the bird's habitat. *Piper*, from its chirping call. **Baird's S.,** *Calidris bairdii.* **Bartram's S.,** *Bartramia longicauda.* **Bonaparte's S.,** *Calidris fuscicollis.* After the Italian ornithologist, Prince Charles Bonaparte of Canino (1803–1857). **Broad-billed S.,** *Līmicola falcinellus falcinellus.* Its bill broadens towards the middle, but tapers towards the tip. **Buff-breasted S.,** *Tryngītēs subrūficollis.* The whole of its under parts are buff. **Common S.,** *Actitis hypoleucos.* **Curlew-S.,** *Calidris testācea.* Its bill curves downwards like the curlew's. **Green S.,** *Tringa ōchropus.* The only green part of the bird is its legs, but various parts of its plumage are olive-brown. **Grey-rumped S.,** *Heteroscelus incānus brevipes.* The name is hardly appropriate as the whole of the bird's upper parts are greyish. **Marsh-S.,** *Tringa stagnātilis.* **Pectoral S.,** **American,** *Calidris melanōtos.* *Pectoral,* because the male puffs out its gullet like a pouter-pigeon, when displaying to the female. *American,* breeds in N. America and N. Siberia, winters mainly in S. America. **Pectoral S., Siberian,** *Calidris acumināta. Pectoral,* see above. *Siberian,* breeds mainly in N.E. Siberia. **Purple S.,** *Calidris maritima maritima.*

In winter its back has a purplish gloss. **Semi-palmated S.**, *Calidris pusilla.* Its three front toes are connected by a web, which extends to about the first joint. **Solitary S.**, *Tringa sōlitāria solitaria.* **Spotted S.**, *Actitis maculāria.* **Terek S.**, *Xenus cinereus.* After the Russian river which flows into the Caspian Sea, where the typical specimen was found wintering, but the bird is very widely distributed and found at some season of the year in every continent except America. **Wood-S.**, *Tringa glāreola.* Found particularly in the northern forest belt of Europe and Asia.

Scoter. Possibly a variation of *coot*; in support of this there is the fact that the same word *macreuse* means a scoter in the north of France and a coot in the south, and also that in N. America scoters are commonly called *coots* by wildfowlers; the coot and the male scoter are both mainly black. **Common S.**, *Melanitta nigra nigra.* **Surf-S.**, *Melanitta perspicillāta.* From its habit of diving for shell-fish among the breakers. **Velvet-S.**, *Melanitta fusca fusca.* Refers to the male's glossy plumage in winter.

Serin, *Serīnus canārius serinus.* Fr. *serin*; which according to Littré comes from *sirène*, siren; with ref. to the bird's alluring song.

Shag, *Phalacrocorax aristotelis aristotelis.* From its "shaggy" crest.

Shearwater. "Shear" is here used in the sense of "skim." **Audubon's S.**, *Puffīnus l'herminiēri l'herminieri.* After the American ornithologist, John James Audubon (1780–1851). **Balearic S.**, *Puffīnus puffinus maurētānicus.* The Balearic Islands are the only place where the bird is known to breed. **Great S.**, *Puffīnus gravis.* Its length is 17–18 in., compared with the little shearwater's 11 in. **Little S., Cape Verde**, *Puffīnus assimilis boydi. Little*, its length is about 11 in., compared with the great shearwater's 17–18 in. *Cape Verde*, breeds mainly in the Cape Verde Islands. **Little S., Madeiran**, *Puffīnus assimilis barōli. Little*, see above. *Madeiran*, breeds on islands from the Azores to the Canaries. **Manx S.**, *Puffīnus puffinus puffinus.* Used to be found in great numbers on the Isle of Man, but it ceased to breed there about 1800. **Mediterranean S.**, *Puffīnus kuhlii kuhlii.* Confined to the Mediterranean. **North Atlantic S.**, *Puffīnus kuhlii boreālis.* Breeds on islands in eastern N. Atlantic. **Sooty S.**, *Puffīnus griseus.* From its prevailing colour.

Shoveler, *Spatula clypeāta.* Refers to its shovel-like, broad-fronted bill. The name used to be applied to the bird now called the spoonbill.

Shrike. Icelandic *skrikja*, lit. "shrieker"; with ref. to its harsh call. **Grey S., Great**, *Lanius excubitor excubitor. Grey*, refers to its upper parts. *Great*, its length is about 9½ in., compared with the lesser grey shrike's 8 in. **Grey S., Lesser**, *Lanius minor. Grey*, see above. *Lesser*, its length is about 8 in., compared with the great grey shrike's 9½ in. **Grey S., South European**, *Lanius excubitor merīdionālis. Grey*, see under "Grey Shrike, Great." *South European*, found in various parts of S. Europe. **Masked S.**, *Lanius nūbicus.* From the black patch over and behind its eyes. **Red-backed S.**, *Lanius collūrio collurio.* The male's back is chestnut, and the female's russet-brown. **Woodchat-S.**, *Lanius senātor senator. Wood*, the bird breeds mainly in scattered trees, but also in woods. *Chat*, that is, a chatterer, cf. *stonechat.* **Woodchat-S., Corsican**, *Lanius senātor badius. Woodchat*, see above. *Corsican*, breeds mainly in Corsica, Sardinia and Balearic Islands.

Siskin, *Carduēlis spinus.* Danish *sisgen*, lit. "chirper."

Skua. See under *Stercorārius skua skua* in List I. **Arctic S.**, *Stercorārius parasīticus.* Breeds mainly in the arctic region, but in widely distributed places. **Great S.**, *Stercorārius skua skua.* Its length is about 23 in., compared with the 17–18½ in. of the arctic skua. **Long-tailed S.**, *Stercorārius longicaudus.* **Pomatorhine S.**, *Stercorārius pōmarīnus.*

Smew, *Mergus albellus.* Perhaps a corruption of M.E. *semawe*, sea-mew.

Snipe 63 Swift

Snipe. Icelandic *snipa*, lit. "snapper"; with ref. to the bird's long bill. **American S.**, *Capella gallinago dēlicāta*. Breeds in N. America, winters in N. and S. America. **Common S.**, *Capella gallinago gallinago*. **Færoe S.**, *Capella gallinago færœensis*. **Great S.**, *Capella media*. Its length is 11 in., compared with the common snipe's 10½ in. **Jack-S.**, *Lymnocryptēs minimus*. *Jack* may refer to the bird's sex, it being believed once that the jack-snipe is the male of the common snipe, which was called the *jill-snipe*; or it may refer to the bird's size and have the sense of "little"; cf. the use of *jack* to denote a ship's flag *smaller* than the ensign, the jack-snipe being about 7½ in long, compared with the common snipe's 10½ in. **Red-breasted S.**, *Limnodromus griseus griseus*. Refers to the bird's plumage in summer, when its breast is chestnut with blackish spots.

Sparrow. A.-S. *spearwa*, lit. "flutterer"; from the Aryan root *spar*, flutter. **Hedge-S., British,** *Prūnella modulāris occidentālis*. *Hedge-*, particularly frequents bushy places. *British*, mainly found in the British Isles. **Hedge-S., Continental,** *Prūnella modulāris modulāris*. *Hedge-*, see above. *Continental*, mostly found on the continent of Europe. **Hedge-S., Hebridean,** *Prunella modularis hebridium*. **House-S.**, *Passer domesticus domesticus*. **Tree-S.**, *Passer montānus montanus*. Particularly frequents trees.

Sparrow-hawk. See "Hawk, Sparrow."

Spoonbill, *Platalea leucorodia*. Its bill broadens spoon-wise at the front.

Starling, *Sturnus vulgāris vulgāris*. Dim. of A.-S. *stær*; root uncertain. **Rose-coloured S.**, *Pastor roseus*. **Shetland S.**, *Sturnus vulgāris zetlandicus*.

Stilt, Black-winged, *Himantopus himantopus himantopus*. *Stilt*, has grotesquely long legs, longer than any other bird in proportion to its body; 10 in. legs on a body about 13½ in. *Black-winged*, the male's wings are black, the female's dark brown.

Stint. Perhaps connected with the verb "to stint" in its old sense of "to shorten"; on account of the bird's small size compared with its allies, the sandpipers. **American S.**, *Calidris minūtilla*. Breeds in north of N. America, winters as far south as central Patagonia. **Little S.**, *Calidris minūta*. This bird is actually the largest of the stints, being about 5¾ in. long, compared with the American stint's 5¼ in. and Temminck's stint's 5½ in. "Little" is apparently the translation of *minuta*, which is appropriate as applied to *Calidris*, for the bird is one of the smallest of that genus. **Temminck's S.**, *Calidris temminckii*.

Stonechat. That is, "stone-chatterer"; so called from its alarm note, which sounds like two pebbles struck together; cf. the local name *stone-clink*. **British S.**, *Saxicola torquāta hībernans*. Breeds mainly in the British Isles. **Hebridean S.**, *Saxicola torquāta therēsæ*. Breeds in the Outer Hebrides. **Siberian S.**, *Saxicola torquāta maura*. The typical specimen was found in West Siberia, but the bird has been observed most frequently in Russia.

Stork. A.-S. *storc*; perhaps cognate with *stark*, that is, stiff, tall. **Black S.**, *Cicōnia nigra*. **White S.**, *Cicōnia ciconia ciconia*. Its plumage is white except what may be roughly called its wings, which are black.

Swallow, *Hirundo rustica rustica*. A.-S. *swalewe*; cognate with Gr. *saleuo*, move to and fro (intransitive); with ref. to the bird's vacillating flight. **Red-rumped S.**, *Hirundo daurica rūfula*.

Swan. An A.-S. name; root uncertain. **Bewick's S.**, *Cygnus bewickii bewickii*. **Mute S.**, *Cygnus olor*. The bird is by no means altogether mute, but it is more silent than the other two species. **Whooper S.**, *Cygnus cygnus*. That is, the bird that (w)hoops or shouts; from its loud call.

Swift, *Apus apus apus*. The bird has been known to fly at the rate of 100 miles per hour (Nicholson). **Alpine S.**, *Apus melba melba*. Breeds mostly on mountains. **Needle-tailed S.**, *Chætūra caudacūta caudacuta*.

Teal, *Anas crecca crecca.* M.E. *tele*; cognate with Dutch *teling*, which means either "teal" or "production," and is derived from *telen*, to produce; thus the root meaning of *teal* is the general one of "brood." **Blue-winged T.,** *Anas discors.* Refers to the front of its wings. **Green-winged T.,** *Anas crecca carolīnensis.* Refers to a patch in front of its wings; but the name is not very distinctive, as the (common) teal's wings are equally green.

Tern. A Scandinavian word: e.g. Danish *terne.* **Arctic T.,** *Sterna macrūra.* Breeds mainly in the arctic region. **Black T.,** *Chlidonias niger niger.* **Black T., White-winged,** *Chlidonias leucopterus.* **Bridled T.,** *Sterna anæthētus anæthetus.* Refers to the bridle-like, black strip extending from the base of the bird's bill to its eyes and beyond. **Caspian T.,** *Hydroprognē caspia.* **Common T.,** *Sterna hirundo hirundo.* **Gullbilled T.,** *Gelōchelīdon nīlōtica nilotica.* Refers to its stout and comparatively short bill. **Little T.,** *Sterna albifrons albifrons.* Its length is about 9–10 in., compared with the common tern's 13–14 in. **Roseate T.,** *Sterna dougallii dougallii.* Refers to its breast in the breeding-season. **Sandwich T.,** *Sterna sandvicensis sandvicensis.* **Sooty T.,** *Sterna fuscāta fuscata.* **Whiskered T.,** *Chlidonias hybrida hybrida.* From its white cheeks contrasted with the black top of its head in summer.

Thrush. A.-S. *thrysce*; probably cognate with Gr. *trizo*, to twitter. **Blackthroated T.,** *Turdus rūficollis ātrogulāris.* **Dusky T.,** *Turdus eunomus.* Refers to its blackish breast and flanks. **Mistle-T.,** *Turdus viscivorus viscivorus.* **Rock-T.,** *Monticola saxātilis.* **Song-T., British,** *Turdus erīcētōrum ericetorum.* *Song*, the bird excels in this respect. *British*, breeds mainly in the British Isles. **Song-T., Continental,** *Turdus erīcētōrum philomelus.* *Song-*, see above. *Continental*, breeds mainly on the continent of Europe, but also in parts of Asia. **Song-T., Hebridean,** *Turdus erīcētōrum hebridensis.* *Song-*, see under "Song-Thrush, British." **White's T.,** *Turdus dauma*

aureus. After Gilbert White of Selborne (1720–1793).

Tit. Abbreviation of *titmouse*; *tit* comes from old Icelandic *titr*, meaning "something small"; *mouse* is a corruption of *mase*, A.-S. for a kind of bird. **Bearded T.,** *Panūrus biarmicus biarmicus.* **Blue T., British,** *Pārus cæruleus obscūrus.* *British*, confined to the British Isles and Alderney. **Blue T., Continental,** *Pārus cæruleus cæruleus.* *Continental*, found mainly on the continent of Europe, but also in parts of Asia. **Coal-T., British,** *Pārus āter britannicus.* *Coal-*, refers to the bird's black cap and throat, but the name is not distinctive, as the coal-tit has less black markings than the great tit. **Coal-T., Continental,** *Pārus āter ater.* *Coal-*, see above. *Continental*, found on the continent of Europe and also in various parts of Asia. **Coal-T., Irish,** *Pārus āter hibernicus.* *Coal-*, see under "Coal-tit, British." **Crested T., Central European,** *Pārus cristātus mitrātus.* *Central European*, found in various parts of what may be roughly called "Central Europe." **Crested T., Northern,** *Pārus cristātus cristatus.* *Northern*, found mostly in N. Europe. **Crested T., Scottish,** *Pārus cristātus scōticus.* **Great T., British,** *Pārus major newtoni.* *British*, confined to British Isles. **Great T., Continental,** *Pārus mājor major.* *Continental*, found mainly on the continent of Europe and in parts of Asia. **Long-tailed T., British,** *Ægithalos caudātus rosāceus.* *British*, confined to the British Isles. **Long-tailed T., Northern,** *Ægithalos caudātus caudatus.* *Northern*, found mainly in N. Europe, but also in parts of Asia. **Marsh-T., British,** *Pārus palustris dresseri.* *British*, confined to Great Britain. **Willow-T., British,** *Pārus ātricapillus kleinschmidti.* *Willow-*, one of its favourite trees for nesting. *British*, confined to Great Britain. **Willow-T., Northern,** *Pārus ātricapillus boreālis.* *Willow-*, see above.

Turnstone, *Arēnāria interpres interpres.* From its habit of turning over stones with its bill in search of food.

Twite. Imitative of the bird's call. **British T.**, *Carduēlis flāvirostris pīpilans.* Confined to the British Isles. **Continental T.**, *Carduēlis flāvirostris flavirostris.* Confined to the continent of Europe.

Vulture. L. *vultur*; cognate with L. *vello*, pluck; with ref. to its preying on other creatures. **Egyptian V.**, *Neophrōn percnopterus percnopterus.* The typical specimen was found in Egypt, but the bird is found in widely distributed places in Europe, Asia and Africa. **Griffon-V.**, *Gyps fulvus fulvus.* Fr. *griffon*; ultimately from Gr. *grups*, a fabulous bird-like creature.

Wagtail. So called from its habit of constantly moving its tail, not, however, from side to side, as the name suggests, but up and down—in a sense it is a "bobtail." **Ashy-headed W.**, *Mōtacilla flāva cinereocapilla.* **Black-headed W.**, *Mōtacilla flāva feldegg.* Refers particularly to the male; the female's head is less black. **Blue-headed W.**, *Mōtacilla flāva flava.* Refers to the bluish-grey head of the male and the rather duller head of the breeding female. **Grey W.**, *Mōtacilla cinerea cinerea.* **Grey-headed W.**, *Mōtacilla flāva thunbergi.* The colour of its head is much the same as that of the blue-headed wagtail. **Masked W.**, *Mōtacilla alba persōnāta.* **Pied W.**, *Mōtacilla alba yarrellii.* The colour of much of its plumage consists of sharply contrasted patches of black and white. **Sykes's W.**, *Mōtacilla flāva beema.* After Col. Sykes, who discovered the bird in the Deccan, India, in 1832. **White W.**, *Mōtacilla alba alba.* **Yellow W.**, *Mōtacilla flāva flavissima.*

Warbler. The name bestowed by Pennant in 1773 on a large class of birds, which are not all outstanding singers. **Aquatic W.**, *Acrocephalus palūdicola.* **Barred W.**, *Sylvia nīsōria.* From the markings on its under parts. **Booted W.**, *Hippolaïs caligāta caligata.* **Brown-backed W.**, *Agrobatēs galactōtēs syriacus.*

Refers to both male and female, their backs being dark brown. **Bush W.**, **Radde's**, *Phylloscopus schwarzi.* Bush-, the bird frequents bushes and woods. *Radde's*, after the German naturalist, Dr. G. Radde (1831–1903), who discovered the bird in 1863. **Cetti's W.**, *Cettia cetti cetti.* **Dartford W.**, *Sylvia undāta dartfordiensis.* **Dusky W.**, *Phylloscopus fuscātus fuscatus.* **Eversmann's W.**, *Phylloscopus boreālis borealis.* After the naturalist and traveller, Edward Friedrich Eversmann (1794–1860), who was born in Germany but entered the Russian service. **Garden-W.**, *Sylvia borin.* A misnomer; in the breeding-season the bird is rarely found in gardens, and in the winter it shows no special partiality for them. "Garden-" is a translation of L. *hortensis*, and the so-called "garden-warbler" seems to have been confused with the Orphean warbler, *Sylvia hortensis hortensis*, which really does frequent gardens. **Grasshopper-W.**, *Lōcustella nævia nævia.* **Grasshopper-W., Pallas's**, *Lōcustella certhiola.* After the German naturalist and traveller, Peter Simon Pallas (1741–1811), who discovered the bird in Transbaikalia in 1811. **Greenish W.**, *Phylloscopus trochiloidēs viridānus.* **Icterine W.**, *Hippolaïs icterīna.* **Lanceolated W.**, *Lōcustella lanceolāta.* **Marsh-W.**, *Acrocephalus palustris.* **Melodious W.**, *Hippolaïs polyglōtta.* **Moustached W.**, *Lusciniola melanopōgōn melanopogon.* **Olivaceous W.**, *Hippolaïs pallida elæica.* **Orphean W.**, *Sylvia hortensis hortensis.* The common name is derived from Temminck's scientific name, *Sylvia orphea*; the name seems over-complimentary, though the bird is a good singer. **Paddy-field W.**, *Acrocephalus agricola agricola.* Frequents paddy-fields in India, where it was discovered in 1845. **Pallas's W.**, *Phylloscopus prōrēgulus proregulus.* See under "Grasshopper-W., Pallas's"; this bird too was discovered by Pallas in Transbaikalia in 1811. **Reed-W.**, *Acrocephalus scirpāceus scirpaceus.* **Reed-W., Blyth's**, *Acrocephalus dūmētōrum.* Reed-, see under *Acrocephalus scirpāceus scirpaceus* in List I. **Blyth's**, after the British ornithologist, Edward

Blyth, who named the bird in 1849. **Reed-W., Great,** *Acrocephalus arundináceus arundinaceus.* About 7½ in. long, compared with the (common) reed-warbler's 5 in. **Reed-W., Great, Eastern,** *Acrocephalus arundináceus orientális.* Same length as the (common) great reed-warbler. **Rufous W.,** *Agrobatēs galactōtēs galactotes.* Refers to the reddish-brown back of both male and female. **Rüppell's W.,** *Sylvia rüppelli.* **Sardinian W.,** *Sylvia melanocephala melanocephala.* The typical specimen was discovered in Sardinia, but the bird breeds all over the Mediterranean region. **Savi's W.,** *Lōcustella luscinioidēs luscinioides.* After the Italian geologist and ornithologist, Paolo Savi (1798–1871), who first described the bird, in 1824. **Sedge-W.,** *Acrocephalus schœnobœnus.* **Subalpine W.,** *Sylvia cantillans cantillans.* "Subalpine" is merely a translation of *subalpīna,* which was the specific name given to the bird by the Italian ornithologist, Bonelli; he evidently observed that the bird frequented the subalpine region of Italy, but, generally speaking, it shows no marked partiality for such a habitat. **Willow-W.,** *Phylloscopus trochilus trochilus.* It does not really show any special partiality for willows. **Willow-warbler, Northern,** *Phylloscopus trochilus ācrēdula. Willow-,* see above. *Northern,* breeds in N. Europe. **Wood-W.,** *Phylloscopus sībilātrix.* Breeds mainly in woods, winters mainly in forests. **Yellow-browed W.,** *Phylloscopus inornātus inornatus.* Has a pale yellowish stripe above its eyes.

Waxwing, *Bombȳcilla garrulus garrulus.* From the resemblance which the scarlet tips of the shafts of some of the wing feathers bear to sealing-wax.

Wheatear, *Œnanthē œnanthe œnanthe.* Two derivations have been given for this name. According to Ray's translation of Willughby the name was given "because (in) the time of wheat harvest they (the birds) wax very fat." Others, however, say that "wheat" is derived from "white," and "ear" from a vulgar name for "rump"; and certainly

the bird's white rump is a very distinctive feature, which is reflected in the alternative name of "white-tail." **Black W.,** *Œnanthē leucūra leucura.* The bird is black except for its rump and part of its tail. **Black W., North African,** *Œnanthē leucūra syēnītica. Black,* see above. *North African,* breeds in N. Africa. **Black-eared W., Eastern,** *Œnanthē hispānica melanoleuca. Black-eared,* refers to the male, in one form of which not merely the ear coverts but the whole throat is black. *Eastern,* breeds in E. Europe and W. Asia. **Black-eared W., Western,** *Œnanthē hispānica hispanica. Black-eared,* see above. *Western,* breeds in the Mediterranean region—the typical specimen was found at Gibraltar. **Desert-W.,** *Œnanthē dēserti deserti.* **Desert-W., Eastern,** *Œnanthē dēserti ātrogulāris.* Breeds in Asia. **Desert-W., Western,** *Œnanthē dēserti homochroä.* Breeds in N. Africa. **Greenland W.,** *Œnanthē œnanthe leucorrhoä.* Breeds in the Greenland region. **Isabelline W.,** *Œnanthē isabellīna.* **Pied W.,** *Œnanthē leucomela leucomela.*

Whimbrel, *Nūmēnius phæopus phæopus.* "Whim" is imitative of the bird's call; for the dim. termination "-rel" cf. "dotterel."

Whinchat, *Saxicola rubetra.* So called because it perches on whin (gorse) bushes and "chatters."

Whitethroat, *Sylvia commūnis communis.* The male's white throat in the breeding-season stands out in sharp contrast to its dark cap. **Lesser W.,** *Sylvia currūca curruca.* Its length is about 5¼ in., compared with the (common) whitethroat's 5½ in. **Lesser W., Siberian,** *Sylvia currūca blythi. Lesser,* see above. *Siberian,* breeds in Siberia and E. Russia.

Wigeon, *Anas pēnelopē.* Fr. *vigeon,* which itself is said to come from L. *vipio,* a kind of crane (Pliny, X, 69), just as Fr. *pigeon* comes from L. *pīpio,* "chirper"; but it is difficult to see how the name of a crane could have become the name of a duck. **American W.,** *Anas americāna.*

Woodcock, *Scolopax rusticola.* So called from its favourite habitat.

Woodpecker. The name is commonly said to refer to the bird's habit of "pecking" the wood of trees in search of insects; but "wood" may refer to the bird's favourite habitat, and "pecker" may be derived ultimately from L. *pīcus*, woodpecker (Pliny, X, 20) or *pica*, *pie*; cf. the provincial name "wood-pie." **Green W.**, *Pīcus viridis pluvius.* **Spotted W., Great, British,** *Dryobatēs mājor anglicus.* *Spotted*, from the white markings on its upper parts. **Spotted W., Great, Northern,** *Dryobatēs mājor major.* *Spotted*, see above. *Northern*, breeds in N. Europe and in Siberia. **Spotted W., Lesser, British,** *Dryobatēs minor comminūtus.* *Spotted*, see above. *British*, confined to England and Wales except for occasional vagrants.

Wren, *Trōglodytēs troglodytes troglodytes.* A.-S. *wrænna*; cognate with *wræne*, lascivious; but why the bird is thus stigmatized is not clear. **Hebridean W.**, *Trōglodytes troglodytes hebridensis.* **St. Kilda W.**, *Trōglodytēs troglodytes hirtensis.* **Shetland W.**, *Trōglodytēs troglodytes zetlandicus.*

Wryneck, *Jynx torquilla torquilla.* "Wry," that is, twisted; with ref. to the snake-like way in which it twists its neck when captured.

Yellowshank, *Tringa flāvipes.* **Greater Y.**, *Tringa melanoleuca.* Its length is about 12 in., compared with the (common) yellowshank's 10 in.